HANCOCK
The Lad Himself

HANCOCK
The Lad Himself

Stephen Walsh
&
Keith Page

COMICS

HANCOCK
The Lad Himself

by **Stephen Walsh** & **Keith Page**

Writer **Stephen Walsh**
Artist **Keith Page**
Letterer **Robin Jones**
Book Design **Robert Hammond**
Editor **John Freeman**

Publisher **Andrew Mark Sewell**
Associate Publisher **Helen Quigley**

More about **B7 Comics** *at* **www.b7media.com**

B7Media

B7Media

b7.media

This edition first published by **B7 Comics**, a division of
B7 Enterprises Limited
Unit 2, Whitegates, Berries Road,
Cookham, Berkshire, SL6 9SD, England.

First Edition

ISBN 978-1-914169-99-1

This book is dedicated with love and awe to the genius of
Alan Simpson and Ray Galton. We owe you a pint, gents.

Stephen Walsh and Keith Page

FOREWORD
Louis Barfe

Tony Hancock's final journey could have come from a comedy script*. His body had been cremated the weekend after his fatal overdose in Sydney on 25th June 1968. His mortal remains needed to be transported back from Australia.

A few nights before his death, Hancock had dinner with cartoonist and comedian Willie Rushton. The conversation consisted mostly of cricket talk, the Ashes then being in full swing in England. When Hancock died, Rushton, who was flying back to London on 1st July, volunteered to carry Hancock's own ashes back home. Rushton was travelling economy class, but the cabin crew felt that this was inappropriate for someone of Hancock's stature, so the *Private Eye* co-founder was upgraded to first class, with a seat right by the cockpit.

Hancock had been in Australia making a television series, his first in colour. It was the last of several attempts to recapture the glory days of the comedian's career. That mobile, expressive face had been ravaged and hardened by years of heavy drinking. Only three episodes were completed before Hancock washed a surfeit of barbiturates down with vodka, leaving a series of increasingly incoherent suicide notes. The last legible note said, "Things seemed to go wrong too many times".

There was, however, a decade in which nothing seemed to go wrong for Hancock. From 1951 to 1961, he stood at the top of the British comedy profession. His days as a name began as the tutor to a ventriloquist's dummy on radio's *Educating Archie*, but soon he was the star of his own show, and it was a show that would set the standard for radio and television comedy.

The enduring nature of Hancock's influence was obvious 21 years after his last BBC TV show, and 14 years after his death, when a nine-year-old comedy fan, raised on his grandfather's Goon Show LPs, first saw a clip of *The Blood Donor* on television. He had always heard talk of Hancock. Mentions of pints and armfuls abounded in daily discourse. He came from that sort of family.

Just a few minutes of grainy black and white footage were enough. This boy had recently seen and adored the first series of *The Young Ones*, and yet Hancock still made him laugh. His comedy of vanity and the dignity of failure was timeless. For his next birthday, that same comedy fan asked for and received the LP of *The Blood Donor* and *The Radio Ham*. Fairly obviously, I was that soldier.

In an age when almost everything is available online, it's easy to forget those days when television programmes, once transmitted, tended to survive in the memory rather better than they did in the archives (don't get me started on that one...) *The Blood Donor* had been repeated in 1976 to mark the 40th anniversary of BBC television, but that had been the last time one of his shows had been seen since 1969.

So, when the news came in the spring of 1986 that there was to be a run of Hancock repeats on Sunday nights on BBC1, I was agog. By this time we had a VCR, and E180s were purchased out of pocket money. Once each tape was full, the erase tab was levered out. These were for keeps**. I must have watched each episode a hundred times. One night in my late teens, I decided to stay up watching them until I couldn't fight sleep for a moment longer. I think I went to bed at around 10am.

Throughout this celebratory time, I had Roger Wilmut's book, *Tony Hancock: Artiste*, out on permanent loan from Epsom Library. My E180s had labels with not only recording and transmission dates, but also the original BBC video tape catalogue numbers. What can I say? There wasn't much to do in Epsom in 1986. Eventually, I bought my own copy of the book, and it remains one of the most frequently consulted volumes in my library. To his credit, Wilmut concentrated on the work, rather than the personal dramas. Also, video tape numbers are cool. Yeah.

All the time I was watching these shows, I was conscious of the sad end the lad himself had met. While it came as the possibly logical conclusion of a sad and protracted decline, it's easy to forget the years before the drinking became a problem, where Hancock was the life and soul of the party. It's also easy to forget that, for better or worse, the industry sailed on a sea of booze. Immediately after World War Two, Hancock was, with Spike Milligan, Peter Sellers, Harry Secombe, Tommy Cooper and Dick Emery, part of the coterie of young comedians who practically (and in Milligan's case, literally) lived in writer Jimmy Grafton's pub on Strutton Ground, Victoria.

Hancock owed a lot of his early radio success to producer Dennis Main Wilson, whose nickname was 'Dennis Main Drain', an affectionate reference to his startling capacity. It was usual to find the producer in the bar with a pint in one hand and a double Scotch nestling in the crook of his other arm as he held forth. As Ray Galton remembered years later, 'Eric Maschwitz was being offered the job of head of light entertainment [at BBC Television] so they took him all round the building, and they said "Let's talk about money". He said "Never mind the money, just give me the concession on the bar".'

Before the darkness set in, Hancock was a bright-eyed lover of life. Enormous fun to be around. An enthusiast, always pushing forward and exploring ideas, though rarely pursuing them to their end (a trait with which I identify strongly). Ray Galton and Alan Simpson picked up on this tendency, which they shared to a degree, and made it part of Hancock's comic character.

The immortal scene in *The Bedsitter*, where Hancock has to recourse to a dictionary for every other word when reading Bertrand Russell, was an amplified version of Galton and Simpson's own attempts at grasping human philosophy. And yet, it's arguable that between them, Hancock and his writers added to the understanding of frail humanity just as much as Russell. So much of *Hancock's Half Hour* is the sound of bright young men testing their intellectual capabilities.

The writers were a perfect fit for the comedian. They had an unsurpassed grasp of bathos. Like skilled executioners, they judged the perfect length of rope for any drop from a mere handshake. Ray and Alan made Anthony John Hancock into Anthony Aloysius St John Hancock, the accretions adding a layer of gentility and pomposity that defined the character beautifully. Then there was the choice of address for Hancock and his ne'er-do-well lodger Sidney Balmoral James (I've just burst out laughing as I typed that. *Balmoral.* Ray and Alan were too good): 23 Railway Cuttings, East Cheam.

As an Epsom boy, I know Cheam well. It is the embodiment of leafy, genteel suburbia. It was always a touch upscale from us. Harry Secombe made his home there, pointed out by my mother every time we went to Sutton on a shopping trip to Shinners' department store. She'd egg me on to wind down the window and shout 'Hello Harry' in a Goonish voice. I told you we were that sort of family. By placing Hancock in East Cheam, Galton and Simpson marked him out as not quite part of polite society. Not quite Cheam proper, dear. There is a North Cheam, but that's basically Morden, and anyway, choosing a real district would have caused uproar in the pages of the *Radio Times*.

Hancock had first encountered Galton and Simpson in 1951 when they wrote for a radio show called *Happy-Go-Lucky*, starring Derek Roy, with Hancock in the supporting cast. The producer of the show was the aforementioned Dennis Main Drain, and the four men hit it off, sensing kindred spirits. A year later, Main Wilson was producing and Galton and Simpson were writing *All-Star Bill*, a variety show on which Hancock was one of a rotating group of hosts.

A year after that, the show had become just *Star Bill*, and there was no doubt as to who the star was, with Hancock, now promoted to regular host, getting his name above the title in the *Radio Times*. Although still nominally a variety show, the sketches were taking over.

Between them, Galton, Simpson, Main Wilson and Hancock were working towards a pure half-hour of narrative comedy with no musical interludes or novelty acts, and in 1954, in the face of considerable corporate resistance, they got their way, with *Hancock's Half Hour*.

Although Hancock knew and relished the weight of words, a large part of his comic gift was in his reactions, hugely influenced by his hero Sid Field. Jimmy Edwards, with whom Hancock worked on stage extensively throughout the 1950s, said that Hancock could ad lib beautifully with just his eyes. It was a measure of Ray and Alan's greatness that they could capture and convey such a visual comedian's essence in radio. This was undoubtedly aided by audiences laughing at the reaction they saw in the studio.

When they moved to television, however, the writers knew what they had to do. They wrote in the pauses and let Hancock do the rest, captured by director Duncan Wood's always perfect choice of shots. It was the earliest days of the medium, but all seemed to show an instinctive grasp of its possibilities. The most obvious example is in *The Reunion Party*, where Hancock is trying to remember the name of a former comrade-in-arms. For nearly thirty wordless seconds, his face registers perfectly and hilariously the gamut of emotions experienced when trying to retrieve a piece of information lost down the back of life's radiator.

When I got older (note that I don't say when I grew up, because I still haven't, and I don't think Hancock, Galton or Simpson ever truly did), I applied my childhood of immersion in archive television to good effect and have spent the last 20 years earning not quite a living as a comedy historian. I was lucky enough to meet Ray and Alan on numerous occasions, usually related to Richard Ingrams and the *Oldie* magazine, for which I then worked.

The most memorable of these was when I went to Ray's imposing residence next

to Hampton Court Palace to interview them both. There I was, sitting in the kitchen, drinking wine, while Ray's many dogs milled around and sniffed my ankles, as we talked about Hancock, Jimmy James, Les Dawson, Alan Plater and other luminaries. It remains a treasured recollection. For a dyed-in-the-wool fanboy, it didn't get much better than that. Even Barry Cryer, whose list of credits possibly outstripped 'the boys' (as they were universally known, even into their 80s), felt awed in their presence. He counted them as friends, but was always very conscious of how they, with Frank Muir and Denis Norden, had paved the way for so many other writers to follow.

In what you are about to read, you will find Tony Hancock's story, told truthfully but with great originality. The rise and the fall. Hancock, always reaching, and usually over-reaching, dreamed of making a comedy of the story of humanity 'from the very first plip to the very last plop'. Here is Hancock, from plip to plop. Stone me, what a life story.

Louis Barfe
September 2022

* Indeed, in the fullness of time, it became one in the form of David and Caroline Stafford's radio play, *Hancock's Ashes*.

** Unsurprisingly, I've still got them.

Louis Barfe is an author and former journalist who has written some of the most lauded biographies of classic British comedians, including Les Dawson and Ken Dodd. He also hosts the radio show, "A Roller Skating Jam Named Saturdays", on NoiseBox.

You can follow him on Twitter @AlanKelloggs

INTRODUCTION
Stephen Walsh

Tony Hancock somehow seems a natural subject for a comic - - sorry, graphic novel! He's been in comics before, of course. At the height of his television fame, he appeared in *Film Fun* which also, at different times, featured the adventures of Arthur Askey and even Reg Varney. Since his death, he's been the subject of biographies and even a couple of television films. With the advent of satellite TV and DVD, he seems to be everywhere.

When he appeared on radio and television in the 1950s, Hancock immediately became an archetype. And so he has remained. The writers Ray Galton and Alan Simpson basically invented the sitcom form for him, teasing out the threads of his personality and creating from them a

universally recognisable figure: the ever-aspiring, grumpy, petty, frustrated everyman pitted against society, bureaucracy, jobsworth vindictiveness and whatever you're having yourself; the best and worst of all of us, down to his last shilling for the meter.

WC Fields, Laurel and Hardy, Buster Keaton and Sid Field all came before him. Young Hancock was hugely influenced by them all, just as successive generations of comic actors (Cleese, Fry and Merton, to name a few) have been massively influenced by Hancock. *The Office*, *Black Books*, *Peep Show* and all the other great British sitcoms of the present day are variations on the Hancock template.

When Keith Page floated the idea of tackling Hancock in comics, an affirmative "ping!" sounded so loudly in my head that I had to put down my pint for a moment. It was a Saturday lunchtime in a pub somewhere between the King's Road and the River. We didn't know what form such a project might take, but we were fairly certain that it shouldn't be just some kind of chronology. Books and documentaries have covered that ground before. If we were going to do a comic we wanted to do something that could only be achieved in the comics form.

So we started with *The Lad Himself*. After reading all the books again and watching all the DVDs, scribbling tons of notes and walking up and down a lot, I was surprised one day at the laptop to hear a voice mocking me for even attempting to capture Hancock in something as piffling as whatever it was I was trying and failing to do. I looked around and, no, the ghost of Hancock wasn't there. But he'd somehow come to life as a "character" in my head. And he wouldn't shut up.

So I wrote down everything he said. The "voice" of Hancock became central to the story that started to emerge. I sent off the first bunch of pages to Keith and he seemed to agree that we were onto something. He quickly "staged" the scenes I'd written and gave me a look at the pages. What astonished and pleased me the most was the "performance" he was managing to get from "our" Hancock. So we pressed on.

The anecdotal, slightly stream-of-consciousness narrative allows us to hop around the timeline of Hancock's life. He even meets himself at different times. In the opening section we establish the gap between Hancock the comedy persona and Hancock the very fallible human being. We explore the origins of his comedy and follow him through the Second World War and back to London afterwards, where along with just about every other British comedian of the period you can think of, he almost starved to death chasing a big break that defiantly refused to arrive.

We'll see him in the company of Peter Sellers, Spike Milligan and Eric Sykes. We'll follow him through his lean years to his success as a radio comedian, surrounded by a team of co-stars that included Sid James, Kenneth Williams and Hattie Jacques. We'll watch as he transfers his radio character to television and becomes the nation's favourite. Streets and pubs would empty when his programme was on the telly. Everybody loved him.

But he didn't love himself. While continuing to produce great, timeless work he gradually alienated just about every ally and friend he ever had. Galton and Simpson were disposed of and went on to write *Steptoe and Son*; Sid James and Kenneth Williams were let go and found immortality in the *Carry On* series of films. Wives, friends and acquaintances suffered and sometimes broke under the strain of Hancock's self-destructive nature.

And then he wasn't funny anymore. He was only in his forties when he went to Australia in an attempt to resurrect his television career, but he was so soaked in booze that he looked twenty years older. As Spike Milligan observed, "He ended up on his own. I thought, he's got rid of everybody else, he's going to get rid of himself. And he did."

The Hancock in our book has already demanded a look at the script and caught a glimpse of his fate. He's not having that. He's not having that at all.

Stephen Walsh,
August 2022

THE PLAYERS

Tony Hancock

Sid James

John Hancock

Lilian Hancock

Colin Hancock

Roger Hancock

George Fairweather

Graham Stark

Bob Moreton

Peter Sellers

Spike Milligan

Derek Scott

Roy Speer

Morecambe
and Wise

Phyllis Rounce

Harry Secombe

Larry Stephens

THE PLAYERS

Cicely Hancock
(née Romanis)

John Le Mesurier

Joan Le Mesurier

Ray Galton &
Alan Simpson

Freda 'Freddie'
Ross

Dennis Main
Wilson

Kenneth
Williams

Hattie Jacques

June Whitfield

Duncan Wood

Wilfrid Lawson

Tommy Trinder

Arthur Askey

Bud Flanagan

Chesney Allen

Willie Rushton

Benny Hill

Edward Joffe

HANCOCK GOES INTO A SOHO PUB...

No7 > PILLARS OF HERCULES < N

WHAT!?

HANCOCK GOES INTO A *PUB*?

WHAT'S THAT?
THE START OF A *JOKE*?

2

5

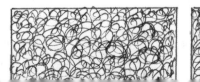
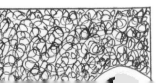

A COMIC?

A BLEEDIN' *COMIC???*

I'VE BEEN IN COMICS *BEFORE.* IT NEVER ENDS WELL...

TELM TON
WEEKLY — EVERY TUESDAY

and TOP SPOT

Here's another mushroom cloud of fun with your favourite double act!

10

QUICK AS AN ATOMIC FLASH THE LADS GOT TO WORK AND BY THE TIME HANCOCK REAPPEARED WITH THE TEA TRAY, THE PLACE WAS ALREADY LOOKING BETTER.

TEA'S UP!

BY THE WAY, DID I SAY FORTY QUID? I MEANT FIFTY QUID.

IN NO TIME AT ALL, THE JOB WAS DONE. AND THAT EVENING, AS THE COMICAL PAIR SETTLED DOWN TO READ, ANOTHER BENEFIT OF THE NEW PAINT BECAME APPARENT.

IT GLOWS IN THE DARK! WE'LL SAVE A FORTUNE ON ELECTRICITY, SID! RIGHT. "HISTORY OF WESTERN PHILOSOPHY" HERE I COME!

THE TURF

12

WHY'D YOU DROP SID JAMES? YOU WAS A GREAT DOUBLE ACT.

EXCUSE ME. WE WAS - WE *WERE* - NOT A *DOUBLE ACT*...

... AND KENNETH WILLIAMS!

DO YOU MIND?

13

NOW -- WHERE WAS I?

OH, GIVE US A LOOK AT THE *SCRIPT*, WILL YOU?

AH. HERE WE ARE.

"WE WERE NOT A... DOUBLE ACT. I WAS THE STAR. HE WAS JUST A -"

14

15

WHAT DOES "JEJUNE" MEAN, ANYWAY? NEVER MIND. LEAVE IT IN.

I'M SURE IT'S WHAT I *MEANT* TO SAY.

THERE'S NO TWO WAYS ABOUT IT.

I'M GOING TO HAVE TO WRITE THIS BIOGRAPHY MYSELF.

I ALWAYS INTENDED TO WRITE A BOOK. SEVERAL, IN FACT.

YOU MIGHT SAY THAT MY CUP OF BOOK RUNNETH OVER.

I MEAN, IT'S NOT *ALL* RUBBISH, LADS. THERE'S A COUPLE OF DECENT PASSAGES. HERE AND THERE. SCATTERED ABOUT. *DISINGENUOUSLY.*

GET YOUR DICTIONARY OUT AND LOOK IT UP!

ALWAYS WANTED TO
WRITE A DICTIONARY,
TOO. NOT COPYING
ANY OF THE OLD
ONES, MIND.

TELL YOU WHAT, LADS.
YOU CAN HANG AROUND
AND I'LL GIVE YOU A
SHOUT IF I NEED A
HAND. AS I SAY, SOME
BITS HERE AREN'T TOO
BAD. QUITE PROMISING,
IN PLACES.

BUT THE *END*...

SURELY WE CAN COME UP
WITH SOMETHING BETTER
THAN *THAT?*

18

22

NOT SHOES. NOT CLOTHES. NOT MY SCHOOL CAP

MY OWN SKIN WAGED A LIFE-LONG REVOLT AGAINST MY BONES. EVEN AT THE BEST OF TIMES THEY WERE BARELY ON SPEAKING TERMS WITH EACH OTHER. AND WHAT NATURE STARTED, RICKETS FINISHED OFF. CAVED IN ME CHEST AND COMPLETED MY TRANSFORMATION INTO THE IDEAL OF MALE WHAT-NOT THAT YOU SEE BEFORE YOU.

WHY ARE YOU TALKING TO YOURSELF?

MIND YOUR OWN BUSINESS.

AWAY ABOUT YOUR BUSINESS, HALF-PINT.

29

OH, WE SEEM TO HAVE A GUEST!

COME ALONG, YOUNG MAN. BACK UP THE WOODEN HILL TO BEDFORDSHIRE!

CAN'T I STAY AND LISTEN?

HUSH, NOW... YOUR BROTHERS ARE ASLEEP. DON'T WAKE THEM UP!

36

REGAL? WASN'T IT CALLED THE MAJESTIC?

DON'T BE DAFT.

OR WAS IT CALLED THE PALACE?

COME ON. I'VE GOT MONEY!

NO. ER – ALLOW ME...

QUICK! WE DON'T WANT TO MISS THE START!

39

DON'T WORRY. IT'S A CONTINUOUS PROGRAMME. IT ALL GOES BACK AROUND TO THE BEGINNING AND STARTS ALL OVER AGAIN.

UPON WHOSE AUTHORITY ARE YOU INSERTING A *METAPHOR* INTO THESE PROCEEDINGS?

D'YOU WANT A TICKET OR NOT?

YES!

TICKETS, PLEASE.

I MEAN, SOME OF THESE FILMS HADN'T EVEN BEEN *RELEASED* IN NINETEEN THIRTY T-

WHAT YEAR IS IT, AGAIN?

HURRY UP!

40

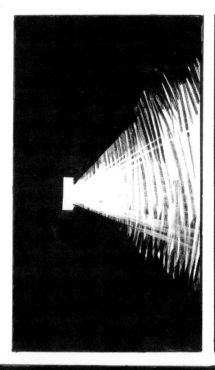

I MOST LIKE WAITING FOR IT TO START. BEFORE YOU KNOW WHAT THE FILM'S ABOUT, I MEAN. IT COULD BE *ANYTHING!* MUM LAUGHS WHEN I SAY THAT. BUT IT'S TRUE. THEY'RE ONLY DISAPPOINTING AFTERWARDS. SOMETIMES. BUT THERE'S ALWAYS ANOTHER FILM, ISN'T THERE?

'ERE...

42

I *SHOULD*, SHOULDN'T I?

I SHOULD SPEAK TO THEM...

43

44

PICTURE'S ABOUT TO START.

WILL HAY IN "WHISKERS AHOY"

WITH GRAHAM MOFFATT AND MOORE MARRIOTT

NOW THEN, BOYS. IF I HAVE THREE BARRELS OF BEER, EACH CONTAINING SIXTY-SIX PINTS, AND I DRINK 37% OF FIVE - EIGHTHS OF THE SECOND BARREL... WHAT DO I GET?

A HANGOVER!

45

46

THAT'S *THREE* CHEMISTRY LABS YOU'VE DESTROYED THIS WEEK, LACKWIT. YOU GIVE ME NO CHOICE BUT TO SEVER YOUR TENURE.

MY *WHAT*, HEADMASTER?

OH, AND BY THE WAY... YOU'VE INHERITED AN ISLAND. THEY SAY IT'S HAUNTED. BUT THERE'S ONE CONDITION...

WHAT CONDITION? I'M IN *PERFECT* CONDTION!

IN ORDER TO INHERIT, YOU MUST GROW A *MOUSTACHE*...

THEY SAY THERE'S A *LOST GOLD MINE* ON THE ISLAND, AS WELL, AND A *DEMON* WHO WALKS ABOUT IN A SUIT OF ARMOUR...

47

50

HANG ON. WHAT YEAR ARE WE TALKING ABOUT? OR IS THIS MORE... ARTISTIC LICENCE?

MY DAD'S HILARIOUS. HE NEVER BUYS A WHOLE PACKET OF CIGARETTES. *"YOU NEVER KNOW"*, HE SAYS. AND WHEN WE GO ON HOLIDAY HE NEVER PUTS ENOUGH PETROL IN THE CAR FOR THE WHOLE TRIP. *"YOU NEVER KNOW!"* I SAY TO HIM –

MISTER PUNCH!

WHAT?

"LO! 'TIS A GALA NIGHT WITHIN THE LONESOME LATTER YEARS!

"AN ANGEL THRONG, BEWINGED, BEDIGHT IN VEILS, AND DROWNED IN TEARS, SIT IN A THEATRE, TO SEE...

52

YOU DON'T OUGHT TO GO TO THE *PICTURES*...

YOU OUGHT TO *STUDY.* GET YOUR EXAMS.

YOU DON'T WANT TO END UP LIKE *THAT* BLOKE, DO YOU?

59

60

TOUCH HIM, TONE. I DARE YOU.

DUNNO. LOOKS A BIT *MALIGNANT* TO ME.

WOT'S MALI- MALIG - ?

YOU AND YOUR BIG WORDS, TONE. YOU'RE LIKE WC FIELDS!

INDUBITABLY!

IN-DUBADUB DUB!

OR GROUCHO MARX!

I LIKE HARPO.

THE MARX BROTHERS! THINK OF IT. WE COULD BE *THE HANCOCK BROTHERS!* COLIN, ANTHONY AND ROGER!

CAN I BE HARPO?

WE'LL NEED ABOUT TEN MINUTES OF SOLID MATERIAL. DAD ALWAYS SAID YOU NEED A GOOD TEN MINUTES. CROSS-TALK AND A SONG. I'M NOT SINGING. YOU CAN SING, COLIN. I'M NOT DANCING, EITHER. NOT WITH *MY* FEET.

HARPO PLAYS THE HARP.

IF IT'S ALL THE SAME TO YOU, TONE, I WON'T BE GOING INTO SHOW-BUSINESS. I HAVE IDEAS OF MY OWN.

REALLY? AND WHAT MIGHT THEY BE?

YOU KNOW ME AND AEROPLANES. I'M GOING TO JOIN THE R.A.F.

THAT'S MY TENT. HIM'S MY PUPPET. D'YOU LIKE MR. PUNCH?

NO.

ANYWAY. WHAT WAS THAT HE WAS SAYING JUST NOW?

WHAT WAS WHAT *WHO* WAS SAYING?

YOUR MALIGNANT PUPPET, OF COURSE! HE WAS SPOUTING SOME OLD GOTHIC ROT JUST NOW. FAIR TOOK THE BLOOM OFF ME AFTERNOON IT DID.

DON'T KNOW WHAT YOU'RE ON ABOUT, SON.

DON'T GIVE ME THAT! *IT SPOKE!*

I WERE UP THE PROM, BUYING ME HALF OUNCE OF SHAG. IF OLD MR. PUNCH HAD WORDS WITH YOU, THAT'S BETWEEN YOU AND HIM.

DO YOU TAKE ME FOR A *COMPLETE* IDIOT?

YOUR PALPABLY CULPABLE SILENCE HAS SPOKEN A MOUTHFUL, SIR. I SHALL AIMLESSLY PERAMBULATE NO FURTHER ALONG THIS FRUITLESS CONVERSATIONAL COURSE AND BID YOU A LESS THAN FOND ADIEU!

IS THAT WC FIELDS YOU'RE DOING?

IT MIGHT BE.

ONCE THE CITY GETS INTO A BUH-HOY'S SUH-HYSTEM HE LOSES HIS A-HANKERIN' FOR THE CA-HUNTRY.

DON'T FORGET YOUR MOOSE HORN, PA!

HE LOOKS AROUND AT THE CAMERA AND YOU KNOW WHAT HE'S THINKING. EVERYBODY'S AGAINST HIM. I DON'T LIKE CHARLIE CHAPLIN, THOUGH. I USED TO, BUT NOT ANYMORE. HE WANTS US TO FEEL SORRY FOR HIM. FIELDS JUST KEEPS GOING. LAUREL AND HARDY, TOO.

GEORGE FAIRWEATHER WAS MY DAD'S OLD COMEDY PARTNER.

YOU GET THE FEELING WITH LAUREL AND HARDY - AND WITH FIELDS, TOO - THAT WHEN THE FILM STOPS THEY'RE STILL OUT THERE SOMEWHERE, BATTLING ON. IT'S REAL, SOMEHOW. WITH CHAPLIN I THINK HE JUST TAKES OFF HIS HAT AND HIS MOUSTACHE AT THE END OF THE DAY AND - I DUNNO...

CHASES LITTLE GIRLS.

BARBER BY TRADE. GOSSIP BY NATURE.

WHAT?

WORD IS, HE LIKES 'EM YOUNG.

67

CRIKEY.

YOUR MUM SAYS YOU'RE DEAD SET ON BECOMING A COMIC.

SHE'S ASKED ME TO GIVE YOU A FEW TIPS, BEING AS I WAS SO WELL ACQUAINTED WITH YOUR DAD IN THE BUSINESS. SEMI-PROFESSIONAL WE WERE, AT TIMES.

WELL. THAT IS. I AM. MORE OR LESS. BARRING ANY - UM - EVENTUALITIES. AS SUCH.

I'M ALL EARS, GEORGE. AND FEET. BUT I CAN'T SPEAK FOR MY KNEES.

ARE WE GOING TO CRACK JOKES ALL DAY, OR ARE WE GOING TO TALK ABOUT COMEDY?

YOUR DAD NEVER LOST IT. EVEN RIGHT AT THE END, WHEN HE WAS FADING, HE ONLY GRABS THE BED SHEET, WRAPS IT AROUND HIMSELF AND SAYS: *LOOK! GANDHI!*

68

69

70

LADY GOES INTO A DOCTOR'S OFFICE. SHE SAYS IS THIS THE VET? HE SAYS NO, I'M THE DOCTOR. SHE SAYS WOULD YOU MIND HAVING A LOOK AT MY PUSSY ANYWAY?

AND WHAT SORT OF A PERFORMANCE DO YOU CALL *THAT*?

THAT WAS A SEMI-PROFESSIONAL COMIC TURN, I'LL HAVE YOU KNOW.

SUCH A PITY ABOUT YOU, HANCOCK. I KNEW YOUR FATHER WELL.

71

WELL, YOU *TOLD* ME TO GET AN IMAGE LIKE MAX MILLER..!

I DIDN'T SAY *COPY* MAX MILLER! DO YOUR OWN THING!

I DON'T EVEN *LIKE* DIRTY JOKES.

AND ANOTHER THING... YOUR *ARMS.*

DANGER MINES

WHAT ABOUT THEM?

THEY MOVE TOO MUCH. IT DISTRACTS THE AUDIENCE. THEY DON'T KNOW WHERE TO LOOK.

I CAN'T HELP IT IF I'M NERVOUS...

TRY PUTTING YOUR HANDS IN YOUR POCKETS.

72

73

SEEMS A SHAME TO TAKE ALL THE RAILINGS AWAY...

THEY'RE GOING TO MELT THEM DOWN AND MAKE SPITFIRES, MUM.

BY THE WAY, I'VE DECIDED TO BECOME A FIGHTER PILOT.

THOUGHT YOU WERE GOING TO BE THE CAPTAIN OF A SUBMARINE?

I AM OF THE OPINION THAT I'D BE BEST DEPLOYED ON THE SKY-BLUE FRONT LINE OF BRITAIN'S DEFENCES, MOTHER. STUKAS GOING DOWN IN FLAMES, LEFT AND RIGHT. PICTURE IT. ARE YOU PICTURING IT?

BUT I SHALL OF COURSE POSTPONE MY PARTICIPATION IN THE BATTLE FOR CIVILISATION UNTIL SUCH TIME AS I'M A HEADLINE ACT AND THE BBC HAVE PUT ME ON THE WIRELESS.

THERE'LL BE A LOT OF PUBLICITY, OF COURSE. I CAN SEE THE HEADLINES: "NATION'S TOP FUNNYMAN PRANGS ANOTHER HEINKEL"...!

ANTHONY...

HERE SHE IS, FOLKS! THE HERO'S MOTHER! ENCOURAGED HIM EVERY STEP OF THE WAY. THROUGH THICK AND THIN AND BACK AGAIN.

ANTHONY. IT'S A *JOB*...

A BOOKING? AN ENGAGEMENT? WHAT IS IT? *MY ACT!* I'LL NEED NEW MATERIAL. THE OPENING NEEDS WORK AND MY FINISH HAS ALWAYS WOBBLED. WHAT'S THE VENUE?

THE PEMBROKE...

75

THE PEMBROKE? THAT'S A *PUB.* I DIDN'T KNOW THEY PUT SHOWS ON THERE...

THEY DON'T. IT'S JUST A JOB. THEY NEED A NEW CELLAR MAN...

YOU'VE NOT SETTLED IN ANY OF YOUR OTHER JOBS, PET. YOU NEED SOMETHING STEADY.

I WON'T DO IT! I *WON'T!* YOU CAN'T MAKE ME!

EXILED! BEREFT! CONDEMNED TO SORT EMPTY BOTTLES FOREVER!

76

77

FRIENDS!

ROMANS!

COUNTRYMEN!

I COME TO BURY HAMLET, NOT TO TAKE ARMS AGAINST A SEA OF - OF -

DON'T TELL ME. I'LL REMEMBER IT.

WE FEW! WE HAPPY FEW! HE TODAY THAT SHEDS HIS BLOOD WITH ME TODAY TO DIE, TO SLEEP. PERCHANCE TO DREAM. AYE, THERE'S THE RUB! THE VALIANT COWARD NEVER TASTES OF DEATH BUT ONCE AND - I SAY! - THIS *IS* A NICE DROP OF PORT.

ARE YOU ALL RIGHT, ANTHONY? DO YOU THINK YOU MIGHT NEED TO STEP OUT AND GET SOME AIR?

78

WHO'S A NAUGHTY BOY, THEN?

HOW MANY JOBS IS THAT YOU'VE LOST, EH? YOU FIT *NOWHERE*, YOU GREAT LUMP. AND ALL YOUR JOKES ARE *STOLEN*.

CAN'T EVEN REMEMBER YOUR BLOODY SHAKESPEARE! I MEAN, EVEN THE *SMALLEST* KIDS IN SCHOOL KNOW THEIR SHAKESPEARE...

I'LL DO ME BASIC TRAINING ON A TIGER MOTH, I EXPECT. THEN IT'LL BE STRAIGHT ON TO THE SPITS. IT'S THE MERLIN ENGINE, YOU KNOW. GIVES IT THE EDGE. YOUR MESSERSCHMITT, HAS THE SPEED. BUT IT CAN'T HOLD A CANDLE TO THE SPITFIRE WHEN IT COMES TO MANOEUVRABILITY.

HAVE A GOOD LISTEN, DOC. NOTHING AMISS THERE!

SO... WHICH WAY TO THE PILOTS' MESS?

I'M AFRAID YOU'RE UNSUITABLE MATERIAL FOR FLIGHT TRAINING, HALFCOCK.

WHAT?

82

83

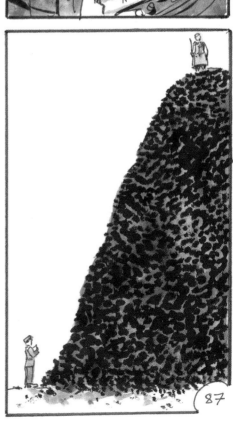

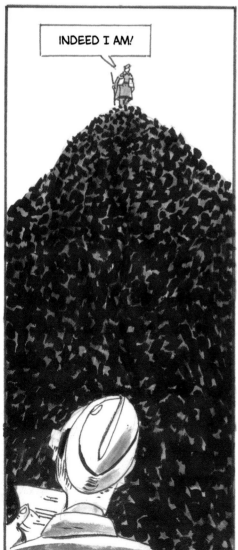

88

89

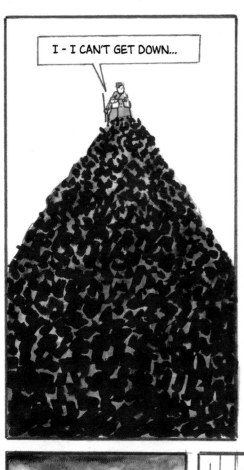

I - I CAN'T GET DOWN...

WHY NOT? IT'S JUST LIKE CLIMBING, ONLY IN REVERSE.

YOU CAN HAVE THAT FOR FREE. AS A JOKE. D'YOU THINK IT'S FUNNY? YOU BEING A COMEDIAN AND EVERYTHING?

HILARIOUS.

91

93

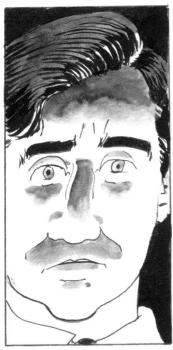

ANYTIME YOU'RE READY.

- AK!

-UURRRRG - G - GK!

IT'S ORIGINAL. I LIKE IT. *NEXT!*

95

'ERE! WHERE'S THE WINDOW?

IT'S CALLED A PORTHOLE...

BUT WHERE IS IT?

WELL, CLEARLY, IT'S...

YES? OUT WITH IT!

...SOMEWHERE ELSE.

BOB MORETON, LADIES AND GENTLEMEN.

WE WERE ALL OVER THE MEDITERRANEAN THEATRE OF WAR TOGETHER. VERY FUNNY MAN.

HE SURVIVED THE WAR, I'M HAPPY TO SAY. THEN HE WENT ON THE RADIO, WHERE HE MADE QUITE A SUCCESS OF HIMSELF.

THEN HE –

WELL, HE WENT TO – TO AUSTRALIA... WHERE IT APPEARS THAT HE...

...KILLED HIMSELF.

SHOW ME THAT BLOODY SCRIPT AGAIN.

LOOK, I UNDERSTOOD THE DIGRESSION WITH THE FLIPPIN' COAL. IT'S A METAPHOR. I'M NOT DAFT. I'VE READ SMUT IN THE ORIGINAL FRENCH. BUT —

HERE. COME ON. BACK TO THE *ACTUAL* STORY. GANG SHOWS FOR THE TROOPS.

(AS IF THE POOR SODS HADN'T ALREADY SUFFERED ENOUGH)

"WE'RE RIDING ALONG ON THE CREST OF A WAVE — "

— WAVE ♫

AND WHAT SAYS MOTHER NATURE'S GOLDEN BOY IN THE CORNER?

LITTLE BIT LABOURED, TONY, IF YOU DON'T MIND ME SAYING SO. BIT WOBBLY IN THE SCENE - SETTING AS WELL, IF I'M TO BE COMPLETELY HONEST WITH YOU...

GRAHAM STARK. ONE OF THE GREAT STRAIGHT-MEN. I LIKE GRAHAM. HE -

HANG ON...

WAS SELLERS EVEN THERE? I KNOW GRAHAM WAS...

BUT I THOUGHT I MET SELLERS LATER, AFTER PEACE BROKE OUT?

WELL, IF YOU'RE GOING TO REWRITE MY LIFE THERE'S ONE OR TWO OTHER BITS AND PIECES YOU CAN LOOK AT AS WELL...

I'LL GIVE YOU A SHOUT WHEN WE COME TO THEM.

RIGHT. CARRY ON.

THE WAR IS OVER BUT THE ARMY STILL HASN'T LET ME OUT OF ITS CLUTCHES.

MISTER DE HANCOCK, LOVE. WOULD YOU MIND SLIPPING INTO THIS FROCK FOR ME WHILE I TAKE YOU IN?

I'VE BEEN TAKEN IN BY BETTER THAN YOU, MISTER DE SELLERS. AND DID I GET AS MUCH AS A TEN BOB NOTE FOR ME TROUBLE?

THE INJUSTICE OF IT, MISTER DE HANCOCK! THAT TWO SUCH FRUITFUL TALENTS AS OURSELVES SHOULD LANGUISH AT HIS MAJESTY'S PLEASURE WHEN THERE'S A WHOLE WORLD OUT THERE READY TO BE PINCHED ON THE BUM!

99

THAT'S IT. I'M GOING FOR A DRINK.

ONLY PLACE OPEN IS THE OFFICERS' MESS. THEY WON'T OPEN *THAT* DOOR TO THE LIKES OF US...

THEN WE MUST NEEDS SELF-PROMOTE OURSELVES TO THE APPROPRIATE RANK, MY LITTLE CHICKADEE.

OHO!

EVENING, SIR. EVENING, SIR. WHAT CAN I GET YOU, SIRS?

DOUBLE PINK GIN. AND THROW A WHITE GIN INTO THE GLASS AS WELL, WHILE YOU'RE AT IT. BUT KEEP 'EM SEPARATE. I WON'T HAVE 'EM MIXED. I DIDN'T DIE AT RORKE'S DRIFT ONLY TO SEE ME DRINKS *ADULTERATED.*

MINE'S A PINT.

GAD, BUT THE BLOOD FAIR STOOD TO ATTENTION AS THE CAVALRY FLANKED OUT AND CHARGED AT JUTLAND. YOU WERE THERE, PULES-HANCOCK. HOW WAS IT FOR YOU?

WET. VERY WET.

CANNONS TO THE RIGHT OF THEM! ZEPPELINS TO THE LEFT! TIGER TANKS AND COSSACKS OVERHEAD! BUT THE LINE NEVER BROKE! A *TOAST*, GENTLEMEN, TO THE POOR BLOODY INFANTRY!

100

AS YOU WERE, CHEPS.

JUST WANT TO SAY THAT YOU CHEPS ARE THE ABSOLUTE BEES-KNEES AND, I THINK I CAN SAY WITHOUT FEAR OF CONTRADICTION, THE CAT'S PYJAMAS.

NOW, SOMETIMES WE OFFICERS FORGET THAT. NOT ME. AND I WANT YOU TO KNOW THAT IF THERE'S ANYTHING ON YOUR MIND - ANYTHING AT ALL - YOU CAN SAY IT TO ME AND I WILL CONSIDER MESELF PRIVILEGED TO HEAR IT.

UM -

WHAT IS IT, MY GOOD MAN?

WELL, SIR, I'M A LITTLE BIT WORRIED THAT THE BRAVE NEW WORLD WE FOUGHT FOR IS ALREADY GOING UP IN SMOKE AND THE SAME OLD BASTARDS - PARDON MY FRENCH, SIR - ARE BACK RUNNNG THE WHOLE SHOW AGAIN, AS USUAL.

102

I THINK I'LL LET YOU HANDLE THAT ONE, PULES-HANCOCK.

I KNEW IT. HE'S GOT NOWT TO SAY.

WELL, IF YOU'VE GOT NOTHING ELSE TO SAY, AT LEAST TELL US A BLOODY *JOKE!*

ANY PLANS FOR *CIVVY STREET*, MISTER DE SELLERS?

OH, NOTHING MUCH, MISTER DE HANCOCK. I WAS THINKING OF GOING UP LIKE A ROCKET AND SETTING THE WORLD ALIGHT WITH ME PARTICULAR COMIC GIFTS. TYPE OF THING.

YEAH.

"ME TOO."

104

THEY LET US OUT OF THE FORCES IN 1946. ONLY A YEAR AFTER THE WAR ENDED. COMEDY MIGHT BE ALL ABOUT TIMING, BUT TRY TELLING *THAT* TO THE FLIPPIN' ROYAL AIR FORCE, EH?

WELL?

SAY IT AGAIN. I WAS CONCENTRATING ON NOT LOSING MY DOUGHNUT IN THE ENDLESS DEPTHS OF THIS CUP OF ERSATZ COFFEE.

THEY LET US OUT OF THE FORCES IN 1946 —

TRY "LAST YEAR" INSTEAD OF "1946". AND DON'T SPEAK ILL OF THE RAF, HANK. YOU'RE IN LONDON.

WHERE DOES THAT LEAVE ME JOKE, THEN?

MAYBE WE SHOULD FORM A DOUBLE ACT. STARK AND HANCOCK.

NOT ON YOUR NELLY. I'M A SINGLE. A SOLO ACT. AND BY THE WAY, IT'D BE HANCOCK AND STARK. IF I WAS TO GO ALONG WITH THE NOTION. WHICH I AIN'T HARDLY GONNA.

GAD, SIR. THESE STALE DOUGHNUTS APPEAR TO BE SOMEWHAT LESS THAN FRESH. I SHALL COMPLAIN!

"ENEMY COAST AHEAD!"

SERIOUSLY, THOUGH...

JOKES AREN'T REALLY YOUR STRONG SUIT ARE THEY?

COURSE THEY ARE! I'M A BLOODY COMEDIAN, AREN'T I?

LONDON IS *FULL* OF COMEDIANS, HANK.

105

EXCUSE ME? I'M HERE FOR THE —

AUDITION. I KNOW. WAIT IN THE NEXT ROOM, PLEASE.

HEAVY SAUSAGE. YOU COULD SURVIVE ON THAT. DRINK TWO GLASSES OF WATER QUICKLY AFTERWARDS AND IT SORT OF EXPANDED INSIDE YOU. YOU WOULDN'T BE HUNGRY FOR DAYS AFTERWARDS.

WHAT HAVE I DONE TO MESELF? I CAN HEAR IT CHURNING, PUSHING UP TOWARDS ME GOB AND DOWN TOWARDS ME BUM. AND IS THERE A MOP IN THE HOUSE? THERE IS NOT.

MUM!

THEY SAY IT'S THE COLDEST WINTER FOR *YEARS*. THE TRAIN WAS DELAYED TOO, BUT ONLY FOR A FEW MINUTES. OH, I'M LOOKING FORWARD TO MY CUP OF TEA. SHALL I POUR, ANTHONY?

107

YES, PLEASE.

HOW'S YOUR CAREER GOING, THEN?

OH, BUSY - *BUSY.* THERE'S A LOT OF CALL FOR VERY HIGH-END COMICS AT THE MOMENT, MUM. SO I'M VERY WELL PLACED, SO TO SPEAK, FOR ANY AND ALL OPPORTUNITIES AS AND WHEN THEY OCCUR.

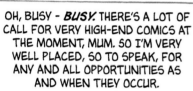

SHE GAVE ME A FIVER...

ALL RIGHT, MY FELLOW STRUGGLERS IN THE WHIMSICAL ARTS... I HAVE *MONEY!* DINNER'S ON ME!

LURDIES AN' JENKLE-MIN. I PRESENT TO YOU, ACCOMPANYING MYSELF ON THE TWELVE-STRING TRUMPET, THE FUNERAL MARCH OF THE HEAVY SAUSAGE. TAKE IT AWAY, MAESTRO!

PUT A SOCK IN IT, *SPIKE!*

BREWER ST. W

RAYMOND Revue bar

SPIKE MILLIGAN... THE ONE AND ONLY...

FANCY A DRINK?

I WAS GOING TO GO TO THE PICTURES, BUT -- GO ON THEN!

CAN I HELP YOU?

YOU SAID *WHAT?*

OH, AND SHE BOUGHT ME A DRINK. SEVERAL, IN FACT. SO I WAS ABLE TO GO TO THE PICTURES AFTER ALL.

AND THEN WHAT HAPPENED?

SHE SAID I WAS A BIT TENSE AND I NEEDED TO LOOSEN UP. A BIT *GRIM,* SHE CALLED ME. IMAGINE HER MISJUDGING ME LIKE THAT!

AND- AND... DID YOU... YOU KNOW...

I THINK SO...

BY THE WAY, I'VE GOT A BOOKING!

BIG SHOW. TRIBUTE TO THE RAF. THERE'LL BE A LOT OF THE OLD GANG SHOW MOB IN IT. IT'LL BE JUST LIKE THE WAR AGAIN.

CHRIST, I HOPE NOT.

♪ INTELLIGENCE IS NOT THE THING I'M FAMED FOR. I MAY NOT BE A PERSONALITY... ♪

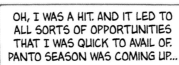

COME ON, *HANK!* JOIN IN!

OH, I COULDN'T. YOU KNOW I'M USELESS WITHOUT A SCRIPT.

OH, ALL RIGHT THEN!

DEREK SCOTT. I'D MET HIM DURING THE WAR. ANYWAY. I STOOD BESIDE THE PIANO AND GAVE 'EM MY OLD QUASIMODO. WENT DOWN A TREAT. SO WE SPOOFED UP A FEW NONSENSE SONGS, WHICH WENT OVER VERY WELL.

NEXT THING YOU KNOW WE'RE A DOUBLE ACT AND WE'RE UP FOR AN AUDITION AT THE WINDMILL THEATRE.

IN YOUR OWN TIME.

TONIGHT - OR RATHER, THIS MORNING - WE HAVE DECIDED, FOR A CHANGE, TO START AT THE BEGINNING AND PROCEED, AS IT WERE, TO THE END.

ARE THESE THE *JOKES?*

I SAID "YES". SO HE TOOK MY WORD FOR IT. VIVIAN VAN DAMM "VD" TO ONE AND ALL.

HE SAID HE'D GIVE US A TRIAL RUN.

112

HE PUT THE COMEDIANS ON BETWEEN THE... THE OTHER PERFORMERS. YOU MIGHT BE CYNICAL AND SAY IT WAS JUST TO BORE THE PERVERTS AND GET THEM TO CLEAR OFF AND MAKE ROOM FOR ANOTHER SET OF SAME...AND YOU MIGHT BE RIGHT.

BUT IT WAS REALLY SOMETHING TO SEE. IT REALLY WAS.

THE GIRLS COULDN'T MOVE. NOT AN INCH. SO LONG AS THEY HELD PERFECTLY STILL, IN *ARTISTIC* POSES, IT WAS ALL LEGAL AND ABOVE BOARD.

HOWEVER, IF THEY AS MUCH AS MOVED A *MUSCLE*, IT BECAME FILTH, AND THE WHOLE PLACE COULD BE SHUT DOWN.

ALL RIGHT, GANG. I TOLD YOU THAT I WAS GOING TO HAVE TO LET SOME OF YOU GO IF YOU DIDN'T MEASURE UP, AND I'M SORRY, BUT THAT DAY HAS COME.

BENNY. *BENNY HILL.* MY BOY. MY DEAR BOY. YOU'RE OUT.

THAT'S ALL RIGHT, VD. I EXPECT I SHALL FIND AN OPENING ELSEWHERE.

113

WISE AND MORECAMBE. WHAT CAN I SAY? SOME PEOPLE HAVE WHAT IT TAKES TO MAKE IT IN THIS BUSINESS. SOME DON'T. SORRY, BOYS.

NOW. DEREK SCOTT AND HANK --

NEVER MIND. I KNOW WHERE THE DOOR IS.

HE KEPT US. HE ACTUALLY KEPT US. HE WANTED US.

AND HE WASN'T THE ONLY ONE. WE GOT MORE BOOKINGS. ALL OVER THE COUNTRY. GOODBYE, HEAVY SAUSAGE!

DEREK DIDN'T LIKE ALL THAT TRAVEL TAKING HIM AWAY FROM HIS FAMILY. BUT WHAT WAS I SUPPOSED TO DO? TURN DOWN WORK?

114

I THOUGHT, A *WOMAN*? AT THE *WINDMILL*?

OI, *TONY!*

WHAT?

115

A LADY LEFT A MESSAGE FOR YOU --

TELL HER I'M NOT THE FATHER!

YOU REALLY STRUGGLE TO DELIVER ANY SORT OF A TRADITIONAL JOKE, DON'T YOU, TONY?

LOOK. DO YOU HAVE A MESSAGE FOR ME OR NOT?

OH. SHE JUST SAID SHE WANTED TO SEE YOU. BUT SHE COULDN'T WAIT AFTER THE SHOW. SHE'S AN AGENT, SHE SAID -

A THEATRICAL AGENT?

WELL, WHAT OTHER SORT OF AGENT IS THERE?

AND THAT, MY FRIENDS, IS HOW I GOT ON THE RADIO.

116

SHOW IT HERE. I'LL SOON GET IT GOING.

NEXT SHOW 3PM

117

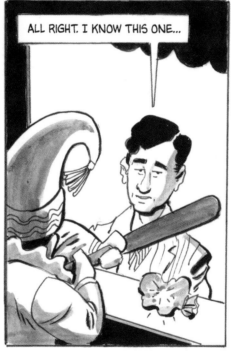

FOR THE *COMEDY* LESSON!

WHAT MAKES YOU THINK I NEED COMEDY LESSONS FROM THE LIKES OF *YOU?*

LOOK. IF YOU'RE GOING TO BE MY STRAIGHT MAN...

ME? SECOND BANANA TO *YOU?*

I'M A STAR IN THE MAKING! A LEADING MAN!

... *REALLY?*

JUST YOU WAIT AND SEE!

SERIOUSLY?

YES!!

WITH THAT FACE? WITH THAT WHOLE... THAT WHOLE... I MEAN, HAVE YOU LOOKED IN A *MIRROR?* AND IT'S NOT JUST YOUR FACE...

119

I'M SPEAKING AS A PAL, TONE...

URGH!

-- AS ONE FOOL TO ANOTHER.

ACTUALLY

ACTUALLY

WHAT?

ACTUALLY, I *HAVE* LEARNED A COMEDY LESSON HERE TODAY!

OH, GOOD. AND WHAT MIGHT THAT BE?

YOU REALLY WANT TO KNOW?

YES, PLEASE

NEVER, EVER, WORK WITH JUMPED-UP, SELF-IMPORTANT, SARCASTIC BLOODY *PUPPETS*!

120

PHYLLIS ROUNCE. MY AGENT. FROM THE MOMENT SHE FOUND ME AT THE WINDMILL SHE NEVER STOPPED WORKING FOR ME.

NOW I HAD BOOKINGS. I MEAN – BEFORE, I'D MANAGED ONE OR TWO HERE AND THERE... BUT THIS WAS *REGULAR WORK!*

WOULDN'T HAVE TO LIVE IN PLACES LIKE THIS ANY MORE. I COULD AFFORD SHEETS AND BLANKETS NOW. AND A BED.

AND I COULD STAND MY ROUND AT THE *GRAFTON ARMS.*

♪ – OH, I CAME DOWN WITH A CASE OF THE GUNGA DINS... ♪

♪ ...AND I'VE BEEN ROUND SINCE BUT SHE WON'T LET ME IN..! ♪

MR DE HANCOCK!

MR DE SELLERS!

YOU KNOW MR DE SECOMBE AND MR DE EMERY –

WHAT-HO, FELLOW NOMAD ALONG THE BROKEN-HEARTED RIVER OF -OF -

– OF KNICKERS!

MR DE MILLIGAN IS HERE SOMEWHERE. LARRY STEPHENS IS WITH HIM. KNOCKING UP A SCRIPT TOGETHER. WHAT ARE YOU DRINKING, HANK?

EVERYTHING.

I'LL DICTATE AND YOU WRITE IT DOWN. READY?

WAIT - WAIT - WAIT! THERE'S NO PAPER IN THIS TYPEWRITER!

122

THAT WAS LARRY. HE WROTE WITH SPIKE. HE WROTE FOR ME TOO. PROBABLY NEEDED A LAUGH AFTER WHAT HE'D SEEN IN THE WAR. COMMANDO.

PROBABLY NEEDED A DRINK, TOO. THAT'S WHAT GOT HIM. BUT LET'S DO THE HAPPY BITS, BEFORE THE... BEFORE THE *OTHER*, EH?

SPIKE AND ERIC SYKES WANT TO SET UP AS A COMEDY WRITING COMPANY. THEY WANT ME IN WITH THEM. SCRIPTS FOR EVERYBODY.

PUT ME DOWN FOR A DOZEN.

AHOY, ME HEARTIES, METHINKS YOU'RE BEING GIVEN THE EYE. AND BY A WOMAN OF THE FAIRER SEX, NO LESS.

DON'T BE DAFT.

DON'T BE SO OBLIVIOUS. WOMEN ARE ALWAYS TAKING A FANCY TO YOU. AND YOU NEVER EVEN NOTICE! WHAT DO THEY SEE IN YOU?

WOMEN? WHAT WOMEN?

TURNS OUT HE KNEW HER. TURNS OUT HE WAS GOING WITH HER PAL, DIANA. TURNS OUT THEY GOT MARRIED.

CICELY WAS HER NAME. ANYWAY, BETWEEN ONE THING AND ANOTHER, WE GOT MARRIED. OH, AND WE WENT TO SEE SID FIELD.

CICELY ROMANIS.

123

124

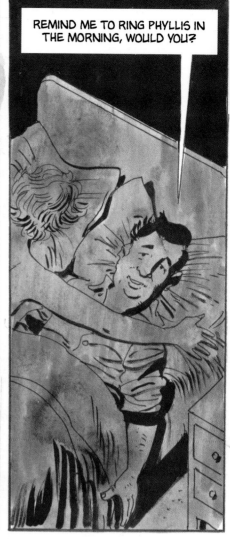

126

(131)

I SHALL CONTENT MYSELF WITH QUIET BEDAZZLEMENT FROM A SAFE DISTANCE, SO. BUT SERIOUSLY, YOU'RE GOING TO TALK TO YOUR PRODUCER?

AS SOON AS HE GETS BACK FROM SICK LEAVE.

ROY SPEER. LOVELY MAN. I THINK THE BAD SCRIPTS DID FOR HIM. THE NEW PRODUCER AGREED WITH ME. DENNIS MAIN WILSON.

"THE EAGER BEAVER SCOUT TROOP"? HOW DO YOU PERFORM THIS STUFF?

IN THROUGH THE EYES AND OUT THROUGH THE MOUTH WITH NEVER A STOP AT THE BRAIN. ANY OTHER WAY LEADS TO MADNESS.

HOW MANY USABLE SCRIPTS DO YOU THINK I FOUND IN THAT HEAP, EH? *ONE!*

WHO'S THE WRITER? ERIC SYKES? SPIKE?

TWO WRITERS, AS A MATTER OF FACT.

"SO WE GAVE IT A WHIRL. AND WE STUCK GRAHAM IN, AS WELL..."

IF YOU'RE SO CLEVER, WHO MADE KING ARTHUR'S ROUND TABLE THEN?

THAT'S EASY. *SIR CUMFERENCE!*

STONE ME. IMAGINE WHAT THE OTHER SCRIPTS MUST HAVE BEEN LIKE, EH?

"BUT DENNIS HAD ALREADY BOUGHT A FEW MORE SCRIPTS OFF THEM. SO WE WERE STUCK."

WHAT DO YOU MEAN, THE TRAM GOT A FLAT TYRE? I THOUGHT YOU WERE COMING BY *VELOCIPEDE?*

NOT AFTER THE LAST ONE BIT ME!

132

SMILE!

IT ILL BEHOVES THE TALENT THAT THE NEWSPAPERS ARE CALLING THE COMIC DISCOVERY OF THE YEAR TO SMILE, I'LL HAVE YOU KNOW.

RIGHT. GET YOUR TIMER OUT AND LET'S HAVE ONE OF THE TWO OF US.

I THINK I'M MOST AT PEACE HERE, IN MY LITTLE DARKROOM. PHOTOGRAPHY'S BEEN MY SAFETY VALVE, I SUPPOSE. MY WAY OF MAKING SENSE OF THINGS. WELL, SOME THINGS.

HANK WAS OFF AND RUNNING. HIS SHIP WAS COMING IN.

HE WAS OFFERED A BIG TOUR. *£500 A WEEK!* TRY RATTLING THAT SORT OF CHANGE IN YOUR POCKET AND SEE HOW LONG YOUR TROUSERS STAY UP.

NEXT THING, HE WANTS TO GET OUT OF THE CONTRACT. HE PRODUCES A LETTER FROM A "PSYCHIATRIST", CLAIMING THAT IT WOULD BE INJURIOUS TO HIS WELL-BEING TO CONTINUE THE TOUR.

HE WALKED AWAY.

ANYWAY. THEN IT'S BACK TO WORK ON THE RADIO SHOW. DENNIS CALLS ME INTO HIS OFFICE. HANK'S NOT THERE.

I THOUGHT I WAS GOING IN TO PICK UP SOME SCRIPTS BY THIS NEW PAIR OF WRITERS, ALAN AND RAY.

133

BUT NO. NO SCRIPTS TODAY. OR ANY DAY. HANK HAS DECIDED I'M SURPLUS TO REQUIREMENTS...

" -- AND HE'S LANDED *DENNIS* WITH THE JOB OF BREAKING THE NEWS TO ME..."

...WHICH REMINDS ME OF THE DISC JOCKEY WHO HAD A BAD BACK...

YES...

IN FACT, HE HAD A *SLIPPED DISC!*

135

I MOST CERTAINLY DO *NOT!*

AND A BIT OF A FANTASIST.

WHAT ABOUT HANCOCK ON THE *TITANIC*?

WHAT? AS THE ICEBERG?

HANCOCK IN THE MONTE CARLO RALLY?

RIGHT. THAT'S QUITE ENOUGH. THAT'S...

... QUITE *GOOD*, ACTUALLY.

CRIKEY.

138

HE SAID THE POLICEMAN LET HIM OFF AND HE GOT A MOTORCYCLE ESCORT HOME. I MEAN, IT *MIGHT* BE TRUE.

WON'T BE A SEC. JUST NEED TO WRESTLE MY WAY INTO THE OLD PENGUIN SUIT.

WE'D BEEN INVITED TO A BIG PARTY BY JACK HYLTON...

JACK HAD BOOKED TONY FOR A BIG TOUR. TONY, OF COURSE, TRIED TO WALK OUT. BUT SOMEHOW JACK FORGAVE HIM. TONY HAD THAT EFFECT ON PEOPLE.

CICELY!

WHERE'S MY PENGUIN SUIT?

"I CALLED A TAXI."

I WAS *PERFECTLY* CAPABLE OF DRIVING US. IT'S THE USELESS EXPENSE I OBJECT TO...

RIGHT! WHERE'S THE *BAR?*

139

I USED TO TRY TO MATCH HIM, DRINK FOR DRINK. MORE FOOL ME.

"HE'D ALREADY HAD A BREAKDOWN. THEY'D SEDATED HIM FOR A WEEK. SO HE'D PROMISED TO GO EASY ON THE BOOZE."

"BUT THE DOCTORS NEVER SAID ANYTHING ABOUT *BENZEDRINE*."

(140)

NONE OF THIS SENTIMENTAL STUFF, NOW.

ABSOLUTELY. HANCOCK DOESN'T DO FEELINGS.

WELL, HE DOES *FRUSTRATION*...

...AND *PRIDE*. WE MUSTN'T FORGET PRIDE.

CARRIED ALOFT ON A CRINKLY LITTLE BALLOON OF PRIDE, WITH ALL THE ARROWS IN THE WORLD AIMED RIGHT AT HIM.

"HANCOCK IN A BALLOON". HOW ABOUT THAT?

ASSOCIATED LONDON SCRIPTS

WHERE'S HE GOING IN THE BALLOON, THEN?

AT A GUESS? STRAIGHT DOWN.

WHO'S IN THE BALLOON WITH HIM?

HELLO, SPIKE.

RAY *GALTON* AND ALAN *SIMPSON*.

THAT'S US.

142

143

144

EVENING, SPIKE.

HILARIOUS.

SHOULD WE GO AFTER HIM?

AND CATCH A WALLOP FROM THAT SPANNER FOR OUR TROUBLE?

I MEAN, THERE HE IS: SPIKE MILLIGAN. THE GREATEST COMEDY SCRIPTWRITER OF OUR GENERATION. WE ARE PRIVILEGED TO EVEN SHARE AN OFFICE WITH THE MAN. AND HIS FLOWERPOT'S CRACKED.

I KNOW WHAT YOU'RE THINKING. THAT'S THE LIFE WE'VE CHOSEN TOO. DOST A SIMILAR FATE BECKON US FORTH TO OUR ERSTWHILE DOOM ALSO, TYPE OF THING?

WELL...

-- YEAH.

BUT HERE'S THE THING... THERE'S TWO OF US.

SO?

DON'T YOU SEE? SURELY IF ONE OF US WENT ROUND THE TWIST, THE OTHER ONE WOULD NOTICE, AND PRESUMABLY BE KIND ENOUGH TO MENTION IT, BEFORE THE LADS WITH THE NETS HAD TO BE SUMMONED?

145

YEAH... ...OKAY.

RIGHT. LET'S BE HAVING YOU. WE'VE A "HANCOCK" TO WRITE. THAT ROLLS ROYCE OF YOUR DREAMS WON'T PAY FOR ITSELF.

RIGHT. WHERE WERE WE?

STUCK. THAT'S WHERE WE WERE. STILL TRYING TO COME UP WITH A FOIL FOR THE LAD HIMSELF...

...THE OPPOSITE OF HANCOCK...

...SOMEONE TO WIND HIM UP AND REPRESENT EVERYTHING HE'S NOT...

...SOMEONE WHOSE VERY EXISTENCE REPRESENTS THE BIGGEST ARROW AIMED AT THAT LITTLE BALLOON WE WERE TALKING ABOUT, BEFORE SPIKE INTERRUPTED WITH HIS TACKLE FLAPPING ABOUT ALL OVER THE SHOP. ANY IDEAS?

ACTUALLY. I CAN THINK OF SOMEBODY...

146

ON THE AIR IN THREE MINUTES, LADIES AND GENTLEMEN.

DAD! IT'S ON IN A MINUTE!

RIGHT. WE'RE ALL SET.

AND NOW, TONY HANCOCK IN...

HANCOCK'S HALF HOUR!

IT'S THE DARKNESS THAT GETS YOU THE MOST. THAT AND THE ENDLESS DRIPPING. HOW LONG HAVE I BEEN IN HERE? THE DAYS AND NIGHTS BLUR TOGETHER...

WHERE IS HE?

THINK HE'S IN A SEWER. LISTEN TO THE WATER RUNNING DOWN THE WALLS -

147

WATER, WATER EVERYWHERE. AND NOT A DROP TO DRINK -

THAT'S COLERIDGE, THAT IS. *"RIME OF THE ANCIENT MARINER."* AND THEY GOT THE QUOTATION WRONG. IT SHOULD BE -

SSSSSHHH!

IT'S *TEA* I MISS, ACTUALLY. HOW LONG SINCE I LAST HEARD THE CHEERFUL TUNE OF A WHISTLING KETTLE? AND THESE PIPES AREN'T HALF UNCOMFORTABLE - OW!

OUCH!

HANG ON. MAYBE IF I CAN JUST TWIST AROUND, I CAN GET MY LIPS TO THE PLUGHOLE AND CALL FOR ASSISTANCE.

HE'S STUCK UNDER THE *SINK!*

HOW'D HE MANAGE THAT?

149

OH, SID. I KNOW HE WAS A BIT OF AN OLD GRUMP, BUT I SHALL MISS HIM TERRIBLY.

MISS HIM?

MISS *WHO?*

HE WASN'T THE WORST. NOT ALL THE TIME, ANYWAY.

I THINK WE SHOULD DRINK A TOAST TO HIS MEMORY.

TO ANTHONY ALOYSIUS ST. JOHN HANCOCK. THE LAST OF HIS KIND. *I HOPE!*

OH, WE MUSTN'T SPEAK ILL OF THE DEPARTED, SID!

DEPARTED? *DE-PARTED?!?*

"HANCOCK'S HALF HOUR" STARRED TONY HANCOCK...

"...SIDNEY JAMES...

"... HATTIE JACQUES...

"... AND KENNETH WILLIAMS.

"IT WAS WRITTEN BY ALAN SIMPSON AND RAY GALTON, AND PRODUCED BY DENNIS MAIN WILSON."

RIGHT. NEXT WEEK'S EPISODE...

CAN'T WE START IN THE MORNING?

SPIKE MIGHT HAVE FOUND HIS ATOMIC BOMB AND SET IT OFF BY THEN.

CHANCE WOULD BE A FINE THING.

I LISTEN TO THE RADIO ALL THE TIME. I LIKE THE GOONS, BUT WITH HANCOCK, IT'S --

WELL, MY DAD SAYS HE *KNOWS* BLOKES LIKE THAT.

"NAPOLEONS IN EXILE..."

OF COURSE, THAT CHARACTER ON THE RADIO DIDN'T RESEMBLE ME AT ALL.

HANG ON...

YOU'VE GOT SID. YOU'VE GOT HATTIE. YOU'VE GOT KENNY WILLIAMS AND BILL KERR...

AREN'T YOU GOING TO DO ONE OF HANCOCK?

OH, I DID *THE LAD HIMSELF* THIS MORNING...

... BUT THE WIND BLEW HIM AWAY.

NOT YOU AS WELL?

GO ON, THEN. DO YOUR WORST.

"MIMES, IN THE FORM OF GOD ON HIGH, MUTTER AND MUMBLE LOW. AND HITHER AND THITHER FLY - MERE PUPPETS THEY, WHO COME AND GO..."

SOD THAT.

I'M GOING FOR A DRINK.

159

BUT THERE'S TWO MORE VERSES!

THREE, ACTUALLY.

YOU'RE NOT THE ONLY ONE WHO CAN QUOTE EDDIE POE IN A DESPERATE ATTEMPT TO IMPRESS.

DOUBLE VODKA AND TONIC, PLEASE.

AND WHERE IS EVERYBODY?

THEY'RE ALL AT 'OME, LISTENING TO THAT 'ANCOCK ON THE RADIO. YOU DON'T SEE A SINNER OUT AND ABOUT WHILE HE'S ON THE AIR.

I'D BE AT 'OME MYSELF, LISTENING IN AND HAVING A RIGHT OLD LAUGH, IF MY WIFE'S SISTER'S UNCLE'S POODLE HADN'T TAKEN SICK AND I HAD TO FILL IN HERE WHILE THE DOG SURGEON WAS SUMMONED FROM CREWE. I RECKON HE'S A GENIUS, THAT 'ANCOCK.

FUNNY YOU SHOULD MENTION THAT...

-- BUT I'M HIM.

160

THAT IS FEEBLE, IS WHAT THAT IS.

BUT I AM. I'M ME.

PROVE IT.

I MOST CERTAINLY WILL!

I --

GO ON, THEN.

YOU'RE NOT MUCH COP WITHOUT A SCRIPT, ARE YOU?

ALL RIGHT.

.... I SEE WHAT YOU'RE DOING. I KNOW WHERE ALL THIS IS GOING.

I'M GOING TO FINISH MY DRINK HERE.

... AND THEN I'M GOING TO WANT ANOTHER LOOK AT THAT BLOODY SCRIPT....

STICK ANOTHER ONE IN THERE, SHALL I?

OH, GO ON THEN.

162

JUST THE ONE.

I FULLY INTEND TO WRITE MY OWN MATERIAL...

-- AND I SHALL DIRECT IT, TOO. *FILMS*, I MEAN.

RADIO IS SO VERY *LIMITING*. I FIND. I MEAN. AND DON'T EVEN *TALK* TO ME ABOUT TELEVISION.

AND IN THE MEANTIME, I'M DOING THE RADIO, THE ODD FILM BIT AND SEVEN OR EIGHT LIVE APPEARANCES A WEEK - SOMETIMES TWICE A DAY - UP AND DOWN THIS SCEPTRED ISLE SET IN A SILVER SEA. THIS BLESSED PLOT. THIS EARTH. THIS ENGLAND.

IS IT ANY WONDER I *LEGGED* IT?

163

IS IT ON YET?

... THIS IS THE BBC LIGHT PROGRAMME...

WE PRESENT, "HANCOCK'S HALF HOUR"...

... STARRING HARRY SECOMBE, SIDNEY JAMES, AND --

'ERE...

HARRY SECOMBE?

WHERE'S HANCOCK?

164

THEY KNOW HOW TO TREAT TALENT OVER HERE. I TELL YOU, I CAN FEEL MYSELF BURGEONING.

THEN MAYBE GO A LITTLE EASIER ON THE WINE, TONY.

THE *VINO* IS THE MEREST EFFLUVIAL EFFULGENCE, MY LITTLE CHICKADEE. A CONDUIT BETWEEN THE OLYMPUS OF INSPIRATION AND THE - THE -

THE *WHAT?*

THAT'S W.C. FIELDS, ISN'T IT? "MY LITTLE CHICKADEE"!

SHE GETS IT.

MY SECRETARY AND BATMAN - *BATGIRL?* - GETS IT. BUT MY WIFE DOESN'T. WHAT DOES THAT TELL YOU?

FREDA ROSS. FREDDIE TO HER PALS.

I'LL BE BACK AT THE HOTEL WHEN YOU FINISH DRINKING. IF YOU EVER DO.

GETTING PERSONAL, NOW. AND IN FRONT OF THE STAFF.

187

CAN YOU HANDLE HIM IN THE MEANTIME, FREDDIE?

I'LL DO MY BEST.

168

... AND THE INTERVIEW IS AT SEVEN O'CLOCK.

WHAT...

INTERVIEW?

169

WHY DID YOU RUN AWAY TO PARIS WHEN YOU WERE UNDER CONTRACT TO THE BBC IN LONDON, LEAVING YOUR COLLEAGUES IN THE LURCH... AND *JEOPARDISING* YOUR FUTURE CAREER AT A TIME WHEN YOU SHOULD BE BUILDING UPON YOUR SUCCESS... AND NOT *SABOTAGING* IT?

LEG IT.

WAIT!

BOOKS!

IT'S NOT SMUT. IT'S CALLED "EROTICA".

BUT I GOT A FEW CLEVER ONES, AS WELL.

PHILOSOPHY, MOSTLY. THE GREAT QUESTIONS. WHY ARE WE HERE? WHAT'S IT ALL ABOUT?

WHAT WILL THE CUSTOMS MEN SAY?

WHAT?

WHEN THEY SEE YOUR SUITCASE FULL OF D -- I MEAN, EROTICA...?

QUICK! FLING 'EM IN THE RIVER!

WHY AM I *NAKED* UNDER THIS FLIPPIN' COAT?

STONE ME.

I MEAN... *HONESTLY.*

ISN'T THAT A BIT *OBVIOUS*...

-- EVEN FOR *YOU* LOT?

YOU AND YOUR BLOODY SYMBOLISM.

THERE'S A JOKE IN THERE, TRYING TO GET OUT. A MUSICAL JOKE. CAN YOU SMELL IT?

I SHALL MENTION IT TO RAY AND ALAN...

THEY'LL KNOW WHAT TO DO WITH IT!

THEY'RE *PROPER* WRITERS!

176

177

ARE YOU QUITE *YOURSELF*, TONY?

WHAT A VERY *EPHEMERAL* OBSERVATION, DUNCAN.

YOU'RE PLAYING THE THROAT SPECIALIST, JOHN.

LET'S PROCEED... SO, HANCOCK HAS JUST GOT THE JOB OF RECORDING THE NEW *TANNOY ANNOUNCEMENTS* ON THE TUBE, BUT SID HAS BANKRUPTED HIM AGAIN, AND HE'S HAD TO MAKE A FEW BOB LICKING ENVELOPES, WHICH HAS DEHYDRATED HIS PIPES AND LEFT HIM *VOICELESS*. WE WERE AT THE SCENE WITH THE THROAT SPECIALIST...

DUNCAN WOOD, PRODUCER.

OH, I AM TERRIBLY SORRY. HOW REMISS OF ME...

I WAS JUST THINKING HOW ALL THIS TALK OF THROATS AND *DEHYDRATION* MAKES ONE EVER SO AWFULLY...

"... THIRSTY."

178

D'YOU KNOW HOW I SPENT MY WAR? GUARDING A BLOODY BIG HEAP OF *COAL*. BUT AT LEAST I WAS UP THE TOP OF IT.

YOU OUGHT TO MENTION THAT TO RAY AND ALAN, MIGHT BE AN EPISODE IN IT.

NO.

I'LL HANG ON TO THAT HEAP OF COAL. MIGHT BE THE CENTREPIECE OF AN EXPERIMENTAL NOVEL I HAVE IN MIND TO WRITE.

ISN'T THE TYPEWRITER A WONDERFUL THING?

SOMEBODY GOT OUT OF BED ONE MORNING AND SIMPLY *INVENTED* IT.

HERE'S A GOOD STURDY VESSEL NOW...

INDEED.

WHAT HAVE YOU GOT LINED UP, JOHN, ONCE THE TELEVISION SERIES *FAILS?*

OH, MY DEAR *FELLOW*...

180

IT'S SURE TO BE A *SUCCESS*...

YOU NEVER KNOW.

MY DAD USED TO SAY THAT. HE WAS THE FUNNY ONE IN THE FAMILY...

HELLO?

I THOUGHT I HEARD SOMEONE OUT HERE...

YES. AH. SORRY TO *BARGE* IN?

THAT'S QUITE AMUSING.

MAY I OFFER YOU GENTLEMEN A DRINK?

182

THEY'RE COMING!

THEY'RE COMING!

THEY'RE -- WE HEARD YOU.

WHOLE STREET HEARD YOU!

WELL? HE'S RIGHT.

THEY'RE COMING...

183

IT'S THE NEW FOURTEEN INCH!

'OW DO! WHERE DO YOU WANT IT, SIR?

SITTING ROOM.

BBC TELEVISION PRESENTS...

IT'S THE SAME MUSIC AS ON THE RADIO!

SSSSSH!

TONY HANCOCK IN...

H-H-HANCOCK'S HALF HOUR

LIVE TELEVISION.

STAMPS?

WE MAKE A QUID FOR EVERY TEN THOUSAND ENVELOPES YOU LICK AND SHUT AND POP THE STAMPS ONTO. *EASY MONEY.*

I AM AN *ACTOR*, SIDNEY. I COULD NOT COUNTEANCE INFLICTING SUCH HARM ON MY VOCAL APPARATUS...

YOU *WHAT?*

ME *GOB*, YOU PHILISTINE!

WHAT DO YOU MAKE OF HIM, OUR DAD? IN THE FLESH, I MEAN.

GREAT FACE FOR RADIO.

AWK!!

185

YOU SEE, THE *GLUE* IN THE STAMPS HAS WRAPPED ITSELF AROUND YOUR VOCAL CORDS AND --

NYARK!!

EXACTLY.

OH, THAT'S FUNNY!

I DON'T KNOW WHAT YOU'RE LAUGHING ABOUT. THAT BACKGROOUND WAS CLEARLY PAINTED. *FAKE!*

HE'S EVEN FUNNY WHEN HE'S NOT SPEAKING!

IT'S THE FACE. HE'S A GREAT REACTOR, ISN'T HE?

THE AUDIENCE RESPONSE REPORTS AREN'T QUITE AS ENTHUSIASTIC...

LISTEN TO THIS. FROM "RETIRED PROFESSIONAL," BURTON-ON TWEED...

I DON'T PAY MY LICENCE FEE TO BE REGALED WITH COARSE INNUENDO AND SUB-NORMAL GURNING. I'M VERY CROSS.

RETIRED PROFESSIONAL *WHAT?*

AND THERE'S WORSE. LISTEN TO "ASSISTANT SIGNAL POLISHER," CLAPHAM...

LEERY SO-CALLED HUMOUR OF THE SORT PRACTICED BY THESE UNFORTUNATE BUFFOONS HAS NO PLACE EMANATING FROM THE TELEVISION BOX OF A PERSON WITH MY PROSPECTS, AND I SHALL UNDERTAKE TO MAKE SURE THAT IT NEVER DOES SO AGAIN. DO I GET *PAID* FOR THIS?

186

AND ONE MORE, BEFORE WE ADJOURN TO THE PUB. "DECORATED A.T.S. VETERAN, CHIPPING SODBURY..."

WITH HIS ITV TELEVISION SHOW AND NOW HIS BBC TELEVISION SHOW, AS WELL AS HIS ONGOING RADIO SERIES, AND HIS CONSTANT LIVE PERFORMANCES, ONE IS FORCED TO CONCLUDE THAT MISTER HANCOCK IS SPREADING THE MARGARINE OF HIS VERY MEAGRE TALENT VERY THINLY ON THE BREAD OF HIS AMBITION...

I PICTURE HER AS HATTIE...

PUB, DID SOMEONE SAY?

STILL...

-- MORE THAN FIVE MILLION VIEWERS. *CHEERS!*

IT'LL BE HALF THAT, NEXT TIME.

187

AND HOW'S *CICELY*?

OH, SHE'S, SHE'S...

YOU'RE NOT... YOU'VE NOT *HIT* HER, HAVE YOU?

WHAT I -- WE HAVE OUR UPS AND DOWNS, MUM, THE SAME AS EVERYONE ELSE...

BUT I'M GOING TO BELIEVE YOU'RE A GOOD MAN, ANTHONY, BECAUSE IF THE TRUTH IS ANYTHING OTHER THAN THAT, YOU'LL HAVE AS GOOD AS MURDERED ME...

NOW. ORDER WHATEVER YOU LIKE.

MUM...

YOU ORDER WHATEVER YOU LIKE. PLEASE. THIS IS *MY* TREAT.

AND LET ME KNOW IF I CAN TRANSLATE ANYTHING ON THE MENU FOR YOU.

RIGHT YOU ARE, SON.

OH. WHAT'S "SAUCISSE LOURDE?"

THAT'S...

THAT'S...

... HEAVY SAUSAGE.

IT'D *WANT* TO BE. FOR THIRTY BOB!

190

"CALAMITIES OF CONSCIENCE, SNEERS MR MR PUNCH..."

"THE DISTANCE RUN FROM STARTER TO DESSERT..."

I SAY! THAT'S NOT BAD POETRY!

RIGHT. NEXT BIT. "THE --

"THE ... SOMETHING THAT... SOMETHING -- SOMETHING AND --

"SOMETHING -- SOMETHING -- SOMETHING --"

WHAT RHYMES WITH DESSERT?

OF COURSE, THIS JEJUNE INSISTENCE THAT A POEM SHOULD RHYME IS OF COURSE ESSENTIALLY A BOURGOEOIS HANGOVER THAT WOULD BRING NAUGHT BUT A WRY GRIN TO THE LIPS, SAY, OF T.S. ELIOT...

192

193

ONE OF THOSE DAYS, EH?

YES.

WE ALL GET 'EM.

HAVE A CHOCOLATE BISCUIT. GO ON.

KNOW WHAT I DO WHEN I'M HAVING ONE OF THOSE DAYS?

YES?

I TURN ON THE WIRELESS AND LISTEN TO HANCOCK.

194

195

196

HAVE YOU SEEN IT?

HAVE I SEEN *WHAT?*

HANCOCK'S IN A *COMIC* NOW!

OH, PLEASE...

BUT YOU *LOVE* HANCOCK!

I HARDLY THINK A... A *COMIC* CAN DO JUSTICE TO THE ESSENTIAL *ECHTSCHMERTZ* OF THE HANCOCKIAN *CRISE DE L'ESPERANCE...*

ANYWAY. IN THIS ONE, *HANCOCK* HAS BEEN SOLD AN *INVISIBLE LADDER*, BY A DOOMED HYPNOTIST. HE'S IMPLANTED A COMMAND IN HANCOCK'S BRAIN, SO THAT EVERY TIME HE HEARS THE TUNE *"OH SWEET MYSTERY OF LIFE"*, HE GOES ALL FLOPPY AND SUGGESTIBLE. THIS GIVES *SID* AN IDEA OF HOW HE CAN FIX A *GREYHOUND RACE*, AND ALSO GET RID OF ALL HANCOCK'S ENCYCLOPAEDIAS, SO HE CAN RENT OUT THE ROOM THAT HANCOCK HAS BEEN USING AS A STUDY TO THE VOLLEYBALL TEAM FROM THE *NURSING COLLEGE* DOWN THE ROAD...

THAT'S JUST LIKE SID!

ISN'T IT!

HE'S THE BEST PART OF THE SHOW, ISN'T HE?

HE IS!

197

NOT STUDYING YOUR *SCRIPT*, SID?

IT'S ALL IN HERE.

LUCKY SOD.

STILL, YOU'VE NOT GOT AS MUCH DIALOGUE TO LEARN AS ME, HAVE YOU?

CAN'T COMPLAIN.

ANY SURPLUS WORDAGE -- CHUCK IT OVER HERE, PLEASE.

HARK AT THE *AC*-TOR. HE'LL BE REMINDING US HE WAS CAST AS THE DAUPHIN IN SAINT GEORGE, NEXT...

SAINT *JOAN*, ACTUALLY. AS ORSON WELLES REMARKED TO ME, WHILE WE WERE REHEARSING --

MOBY DICK. HEARD IT. NEXT.

GENTS, WE'VE GOT OUR OWN REHEARSAL TO GET THROUGH, IN CASE YOU'VE FORGOTTEN...

WELL, WHAT ARE WE *WAITING* FOR, THEN? WHERE WERE WE?

YOU AND SID ARE LOCKED IN THE OLD AIR-RAID SHELTER, AND JOHN HAD THE NEXT LINE...

ME?

D'YOU KNOW, I THINK I *DRIFTED AWAY?*

WHERE DID YOU DRIFT TO?

198

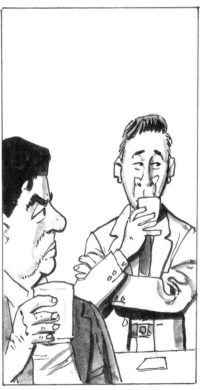

ANYWAY, HE GOT RID OF ME.

I WAS GLAD TO GET AWAY FROM HIM. THE ONE NOTE PUNCHLINE TO SOMEONE ELSE'S JOKE.

NO, I'M LYING. WHEN IN DOUBT, HURT SOMEBODY. I HAVE THAT IN COMMON WITH TONY, ANYWAY...

SO, WHAT DO I *REMEMBER* ABOUT HANCOCK?

I REMEMBER HOW MUCH MONEY HE WAS MAKING, AND HOW IT NEVER SEEMED TO MAKE THE SLIGHTEST DENT IN HIS LUGUBRIOSITY.

HIS *GLOOM*, LUV!

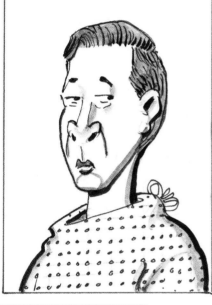

ME? I WENT ON TO... WELL, THE *CARRY ON* FILMS. IF YOU CAN CALL THEM FILMS.

NO, TO BE FAIR, SOME OF THEM WERE GOOD.

I MADE MORE FILMS THAN HANCOCK, ANYWAY. OH, HE WAS GOING TO CONQUER THE CINEMA. AND EVERYTHING ELSE.

IF ONLY HE COULD GET AROUND TO IT.

SHIT, OR GET OFF THE CHAMBER POT. AS A DOCTOR ONCE REMARKED TO ME.

SPEAKING OF MY PILES...

... SOMEONE ONCE ASCRIBED THEM TO MY INABILITY TO GIVE AND/OR RECEIVE LOVE...

I CALLED THEM ALL SORTS OF NAMES AT THE TIME. BUT OF COURSE, THEY WERE RIGHT.

I WONDER IF *HANCOCK* HAD PILES?

DON'T YOU LIKE THE MUSIC?

WHAT ARE THE SYMPTOMS OF PILES?

MY DEAR FELLOW...

-- *WHATEVER* COULD BRING SUCH A THING TO MIND AT A TIME LIKE THIS?

MY ARSE DOESN'T HURT. IS THAT A GOOD OR A BAD SIGN? AND ONE OF CICELY'S POODLES CAN SEE GHOSTS. I WISH I LIVED ON A BARGE.

I THOUGHT YOU PINED FOR A NICE LITTLE ATTIC IN PARIS?

A BARGE *WITH* AN ATTIC, OF COURSE...

OF COURSE!

AND I'LL PUT IN A PIANO, OF COURSE, SO YOU CAN COME ABOARD AND TICKLE THE IVORIES...

HOW *COMPLETELY* LOVELY...

WELL, ARE WE GOING TO DO THIS AWARDS DO, OR WHAT?

I SUPPOSE WE'D BETTER.

202

WILL *CICELY* BE JOINING US?

I'M NOT SURE...

HOW DO YOU DO IT, JOHN? HOW DO YOU AND HATTIE MAINTAIN SUCH A PERFECT MARRIAGE?

SHE'S MOVED HER LOVER INTO THE BEDROOM, AND I'M DOWNSTAIRS IN THE PARLOUR. NEAR THE DOOR...

18 LINA STORES L

WHAT!? HOW DID THAT HAPPEN?

WELL, I'M NOT *ENTIRELY* SURE, BUT IT'S ALL FOR THE BEST...

HOW CAN YOU SAY THAT?

TONY, LOVE DOESN'T GO AWAY JUST BECAUSE THE WIND CHANGES.

SURELY YOU'RE STILL ALLOWED TO *THUMP* HIM?

WHYEVER WOULD I DO *THAT?*

St.JAMES'S RE-

WHERE WERE WE GOING, ANYWAY?

SOME AWARDS THING.

OH, THAT'S *RIGHT.*

YOU'RE THE COMEDIAN OF THE YEAR.

204

'ERE HE IS!

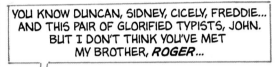

YOU KNOW DUNCAN, SIDNEY, CICELY, FREDDIE... AND THIS PAIR OF GLORIFIED TYPISTS, JOHN. BUT I DON'T THINK YOU'VE MET MY BROTHER, *ROGER*...

DELIGHTED!

HE'S MY NEW AGENT.

OH, WE *MUST* DRINK TO THAT!

'ELLO, PLAYMATES!

THE NEXT AWARD IS FOR "SCRIPTWRITER OF THE YEAR"...

I LOVE SCRIPTWRITERS. WE ALL DO. THEY TELL US EXACTLY WHAT TO FORGET TO SAY!

BUT THE BUSINESS OF COMEDY IS A SERIOUS ONE. IT SAYS HERE. WHO *WRITES* THIS STUFF?

ANYWAY! WITHOUT FURTHER ADO -- DID SOMEONE SAY BLESS YOU -- THE AWARD GOES TO...

ALAN SIMPSON AND RAY GALTON!

WELL DONE, BOYS.

MAYBE YOU OUGHT TO SLOW DOWN ON THE OLD MOON JUICE, TONY? YOU'LL BE UP THERE IN A MINUTE.

I'M GOING.

TONY. MATE.

ENJOY THE BLOOMIN' MOMENT.

RIGHT. IT'S THE INTERVAL. WHO'S FOR A DRINK?

'ELLO, TONE. *TOMMY TRINDER.* SAW YOU IN THE WINDMILL, WAY BACK THEN...

PLEASE. SIT DOWN.

206

DON'T ASK ME WHAT I WAS DOING THERE!

JUST WANTED TO POP OVER AND SHAKE YOUR HAND. YOU'RE THE REAL THING. SID FIELD WOULD HAVE LOVED YOU...

... AND I LOVED THE *TEST PILOT* EPISODE. YOU'RE UP AT NINETY THOUSAND FEET. THERE'S A KNOCK ON THE WINDOW. YOU LOOK OUT AND SEE... *KENNETH WILLIAMS!*

WHICH OF YOU TWO IS *MRS. HANCOCK?*

KENNY'S GREAT. ONE OF A KIND. I'D HANG ON TO HIM, IF I WERE YOU!

LADIES AND GENTLEMEN... *FLANAGAN AND ALLEN!*

207

208

I MET HIM, IN HOLLYWOOD, LATER ON...

"HE'D MADE AN ABSOLUTE FORTUNE. BUT HE'D NEVER READ THE SMALL PRINT...

"NOW HE HAD NOTHING."

BUSTER KEATON WAS THE SAME. *DRUNK.*

HE DIDN'T SAY MUCH. WE DIDN'T HAVE MUCH OF A CHAT.

HE DIDN'T KNOW WHO I WAS. BUT HE KNEW WE WERE IN THE SAME BUSINESS.

BUT HE SHOOK MY HAND... THEN HE SAID --

WELCOME TO THE GHOST CLUB.

209.

AHOY... ...OR WORDS TO THAT EFFECT...

STAND BY TO REPEL BOARDERS!

AHA! I SEE I'M TOO LATE!

I'D BETTER PLY YOU WITH DRINK, SO!

UM... WHERE'S HE GONE?

I'M AFRAID IT'S ALL MY FAULT...

I'M NOT AT ALL SURE WHAT IT WAS IT WAS I SAID, CICELY, BUT HE SEEMED TO TAKE A SORT OF *NEBULOUS UMBRAGE...*

OH, HE'S ALWAYS DOING THAT. *DRINK?*

YOU ON A BARGE? THERE MIGHT BE AN EPISODE IN THAT.

THERE'S A *FILM* IN THAT.

NO THERE ISN'T.

HANCOCK THE BARGEE!

...A GIRL AT EVERY LOCK!

210

IS THIS YOUR WAY OF SAYING YOU'VE FALLEN BEHIND ON THE FILM YOU'RE ACTUALLY MEANT TO BE WRITING FOR ME?

FILM? WHAT FILM?

SORRY TO KEEP YOU WAITING, FOLKS...

-- TRAFFIC FROM PINEWOOD WAS MURDER.

ANYTHING INTERESTING?

CARRY ON CONSTABLE. IT'S NOT IN YOUR LEAGUE, BOYS. BUT YOU SHOULD HAVE SEEN KENNY WILLIAMS' FACE WHEN HE SAW I'D BEEN CAST!

I BELIEVE HE WAS RATHER OUTSTANDING AS THE DAUPHIN IN *SAINT JOAN*...

SO I HEARD! HYAH-HYAH!

IS THAT WHERE YOU'D RATHER BE?

YOU WHAT?

IF YOU WISH TO PURSUE OTHER OPPORTUNITIES --

LEAVE IT OUT!

THAT'S ONLY *PLAYING.* FOOLING AROUND. *THIS* IS THE REAL THING.

RIGHT. DOWN TO BUSINESS. WHERE'S THE LAD HIMSELF THIS WEEK?

A GARDEN PARTY AT BUCKINGHAM PALACE...

211

QUICK! IT'S STARTING!

HE THINKS HE'S GOT AN INVITATION TO MEET THE QUEEN!

THAT'S JUST LIKE HIM.

"ANTONIUS HANDCRANK?"

YES. FUNNY OF THEM TO GET MY NAME WRONG, ISN'T IT?

WHAT ADDRESS WAS ON IT?

OH, HARK AT THE PEASANT!

THAT'S *HAND DELIVERED*, THAT IS!

BY THE QUEEN? I HOPE YOU AT LEAST OFFERED HER A CUPPA...

THE PALACE WOULD NEVER OPERATE IN SUCH A MANNER.

IT'S JUST *FUN*, ISN'T IT?

WE'D BE LOST WITHOUT A BIT OF FUN, WOULDN'T WE?

WHERE ARE YOU GETTING THESE THOUGHTS?

SSH. HE'S OFF TO THE PALACE...

WE TAKE A VERY DIM VIEW OF INTERLOPERS, I'LL HAVE YOU KNOW.

THAT UNIFORM'S WRONG, FOR A START!

212

I, AN INTEROLOPER? YOU'RE GOING TO BE IN A LOT OF TROUBLE WHEN HER MAJESTY HEARS ABOUT THIS, MY FINE FELLOW...

"ANTONIUS HANDCRANK?"

SUCH IS I, YES.

I SAY CLAP HIM IN IRONS, JUST TO BE ON THE SAFE SIDE.

OH, I CAN'T WAIT TO TELL HER MAJESTY ABOUT YOU, SUNSHINE!

WHAT HAVE I MISSED?

TURNS OUT THE REAL ANTONIO HANDSHANKY IS A RUSSIAN SPY...

CRIKEY!

FOR THE LAST TIME, MY NAME IS ANTHONY ALOYSIUS ST. JOHN HANCOCK...

... OF 23 RAILWAY CUTTINGS, EAST CHEAM. A LIKELY STORY.

YOU CAN DROP THE ACT, COMRADE HANDKRANSKI. WE'RE GOING TO EXCHANGE YOU FOR ONE OF OUR CHAPS WHO GOT NABBED BY OUR CHAPS...

WHO ARE YOU CALLING A COM -- WAIT A MINUTE!

EXCHANGE?!?

THE LOOK ON HIS FACE!

QUITE THE PICTURE!

AND THEN HE GOT TO HIS NEW FLAT IN EAST BERLIN, AND SID WAS THERE!

23 EISENBAHNSTRASSE OSTCHEAM!

213

GOOD OLD SID!

DUNCAN?

TONY.

DUNCAN, SID GETS A LOT OF OTHER WORK, DOESN'T HE?

BUSIEST CHARACTER MAN IN TOWN.

SO, HE AND VALERIE WOULDN'T REALLY SUFFER, *FINANCIALLY* IF HE ... IF HE WAS...

I DARE SAY HE EARNS A NICE CRUST, TONY.

GOOD. HAPPY TO KNOW THAT. HAPPY TO KNOW THAT.

PROBABLY BEST IF YOU TELL HIM, DUNCAN.

214

"SO THAT WAS THAT..."

NEVER SPOKE TO HIM AGAIN.

I DON'T MEAN WE *FELL OUT*, OR ANYTHING LIKE THAT.

THE DOOR CLOSED.

RAY AND ALAN WROTE ME A SERIES. WASN'T BAD. WASN'T UP TO THE STANDARD OF THE HANCOCK SHOWS, THOUGH.

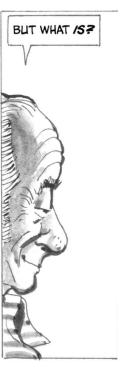

BUT WHAT *IS?*

BEST WORK I EVER DID. AND I WORKED A LOT. BUT WITH HIM, IT WAS DIFFERENT. AND THE *LAUGHS* WE HAD...

THAT ALL WENT, TOO.

I DID SEE HIM ONCE MORE. I WAS IN THE CAR, SO HE DIDN'T SEE ME.

HE WAS JUST STANDING THERE, LIKE HE DIDN'T KNOW WHERE TO GO. I'D SEEN HIM LIKE THAT BEFORE, WHEN HIS MUM'S HUSBAND KILLED HIMSELF. HIS HEART BROKE FOR HER.

SOME PEOPLE DON'T LIKE IT WHEN YOU'VE SEEN THEM RIPPED OPEN LIKE THAT.

BUT WHAT DO *I* KNOW?

ANYWAY. HE MADE ONE MORE SERIES FOR THE BBC...

AND IT WAS *BRILLIANT.*

FIFTEEN MILLION VIEWERS!

215

WE MUST BE DOING SOMETHING RIGHT, THEN.

IT WAS FIFTEEN AND A *HALF* LAST WEEK..

WHAT'S HALF A MILLION BETWEEN FRIENDS --

JESUS!

WHAT HAPPENED TO *YOU?*

BIT OF A PRANG IN THE OLD JALOPY...

AND BEFORE YOU ASK, *CICELY* WAS AT THE WHEEL.

WE'LL HAVE TO COVER IT UP. I'LL PUT THE MAKEUP DEPARTMENT ON RED ALERT.

AND THERE IS ONE OTHER PROBLEM, TOO...

OH?

TONY SAYS HIS MEMORY IS ON THE BLINK.

A SLIGHT CONCUSSION, ACCORDING TO MY MEDICAL ENCYCLOPAEDIA...

ARE YOU ALL RIGHT? SHOULD WE GET A *SPECIALIST?*

ACRES OF WORDS, THAT'S THE PROBLEM.

BUT THAT'S WHAT SCRIPTS ARE *MADE* OF. WORDS.

MAYBE ONCE WE START REHEARSALS?

WORDS.

WILFRID LAWSON. WAS THAT WHO SID MENTIONED? ALWAYS PISSED. USED TO WRITE ALL HIS LINES DOWN AND STICK THEM TO THE SET. THAT'S WHAT WE'LL DO.

216

ARE YOU INSINUATING THAT I AM AN ALCOHOLIC?

WELL?

SHALL WE JUST... "THE BLOOD DONOR"

SHALL WE TAKE IT FROM THE TOP?

OH, FOR HEAVEN'S SAKE, BOYS! I'LL JUST START, SHALL I?

THANK YOU, JUNE. RIGHT, WE'RE IN THE HOSPITAL RECEPTION AREA...

GOOD AFTERNOON, SIR...

GOOD AFTERNOON, MISS. I HAVE COME IN ANSWER TO YOUR ADVERT ON THE WALL NEXT TO THE EAGLE LAUNDRY IN PELHAM ROAD...

HE WANTS TO GIVE BLOOD, SEE? BUT HE GETS ALL UPPITY WHEN SHE ASKS HIM IF HE'S HAD ANY *DISEASES!*

"HOW DARE YOU!"

217

AN' HE STARTS GOING ON ABOUT ALL THE BLOOD HE SHED FOR HIS COUNTRY!

AN' WHEN HE TALKS TO THE SCOTTISH DOCTOR!

"IT'S A BRAW BRICHT MOONLIT THIS MORNING!"

HOOTS, MON!

WHEN THE DOCTOR STICKS A PIN IN HIS FINGER TO GET A SAMPLE!

AN' HANCOCK THINKS THAT'S ALL THEY'RE GOING TO TAKE! "RIGHT, WHERE'S ME TEA AND BISCUITS?"

"A SAMPLE? HOW MUCH DO YOU NORMALLY TAKE?"

A PINT!

"I DON'T MIND GIVING A REASONABLE AMOUNT, BUT A PINT..."

"THAT'S VERY NEARLY AN ARMFUL!"

ROXY

WHAT DO YOU RECKON?

THE REBEL

MAYBE HE'S NO GOOD IN FILMS. MAYBE HE SHOULD HAVE STAYED ON THE TELLY?

TONY HANCOCK THE REBEL

ME DAD SAYS HE SHOULD HAVE STAYED ON THE RADIO!

218

220

"I CANNOT SEE WHAT FLOWERS ARE AT MY FEET..."

"NOR WHAT SOFT INCENSE HANGS UPON THE BOUGHS..."

WELL?

YES?

IS THAT IT? IS THERE ANY MORE?

OH, YES. VERSES AND VERSES. *KEATS.* AND THEY'RE LOVELY. SIMPLY LOVELY. IF ONLY I COULD REMEMBER THEM.

HOW'S YOUR OWN MEMORY THESE DAYS?

I'LL FORGET YOU SAID THAT!

OH, VERY GOOD!

MEMORY IS WHAT GOT ME STARTED. I COULD RECITE WHOLE FILMS-WORTH OF LAUREL AND HARDY, AND W.C. FIELDS.

BUT IT WAS POETRY THAT IMPRESSED MY DAD AND HIS PALS THE MOST.

"THAT MOTLEY DRAMA -- OH, BE SURE IT SHALL NOT BE FORGOT! WITH ITS PHANTOM CHASED FOR EVERMORE BY A CROWD THAT SEES IT NOT..."

221

VERY FUNNY! ALMOST AS FUNNY AS THAT STUFF YOU DID WITH SID JAMES!

BUT DID YOU SEE WHAT THE AMERICAN CRITICS SAID ABOUT IT?

WHAT DO THE AMERICANS KNOW?

WE DON'T WRITE FOR AMERICANS...

EXACTLY!

THERE'S A WORLD OUT THERE BEYOND EAST CHEAM, OR EARL'S COURT...

GOLDERS GREEN?

HAMMERSMITH?

YOU NEED TO STOP BEING SO... PAROCHIAL!

UH-OH. THE LAD'S GOT A NEW DICTIONARY...

LET'S MAKE THE FILM TRULY... INTERNATIONAL.

THE NEW YORK CRITICS COMPARED ME TO NORMAN WISDOM, BOYS...

NORMAN. ...BLOODY... ...WISDOM.

"HANCOCK THE INTERNATONAL PLAYBOY"

ASSOCIATED LONDON SCRIPTS

"HANCOCK THE SPY"

"HANCOCK THE GREAT LOVER"

"HANCOCK THE BULLFIGHTER"

"HANCOCK THE SUBMARINE COMMANDER"

223

"HANCOCK THE --"

"... HANCOCK".

EXACTLY.

HARK! CAN YOU HEAR IT?

SPIKE IS SCREAMING AGAIN...

AND PROBABLY NAKED.

REMEMBER HOW SURE WE USED TO BE THAT THIS BUSINESS WOULDN'T DRIVE US MAD?

WHAT IF IT HAS? WHAT IF WE'RE TOO FAR GONE TO TELL?

IF ONLY!

SERIOUSLY. ARE YOU GOING TO END UP CARRIED OUT OF HERE BY DOCTORS EVERY FEW WEEKS, LIKE SPIKE?

NOT AS LONG AS WE HAVE A TV SERIES TO WRITE FOR THE LAD.

AND A FILM. MUSTN'T FORGET THE FILM.

AN INTERNATIONAL FILM...

THERE GOES SPIKE AGAIN.

THE DAY OFF
A FEATURE FILM SCREENPLAY
BY
RAY GALTON
AND
ALAN SIMPSON

WHAT'S IT ABOUT, THEN?

227

WELL, THERE'S THIS BLOKE. BUS DRIVER...

WE'RE LOOKING FOR THE FULL CANVAS OF HUMANITY HERE, I HASTEN TO ADD.

OF COURSE. OFF WORK FOR THE DAY--

... DRIFTS AROUND LONDON... WELL, HAMMERSMITH. THEN MEETS A GIRL, MEETS ALL SORTS OF PEOPLE...

HE PRETENDS TO BE AN ARCHITECT TO IMPRESS THE GIRL. ALL HIS OPTIONS SORT OF APPEAR BEFORE HIM THROUGHOUT THE DAY...

BUT IN THE END, HE DOESN'T REALLY OPT FOR ANY OF THEM. A DATE WITH THE GIRL GOES WRONG, AND...

HE ENDS UP RETURNING TO THE EVER-DECREASING CIRCLES OF HIS LIFE, AND...

YOU WROTE THIS WITH *ME* IN MIND, DID YOU?

OF COURSE...

TELL YOU WHAT, BOYS. I'LL DO YOU A FAVOUR...

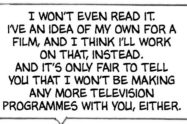

I WON'T EVEN READ IT. I'VE AN IDEA OF MY OWN FOR A FILM, AND I THINK I'LL WORK ON THAT, INSTEAD. AND IT'S ONLY FAIR TO TELL YOU THAT I WON'T BE MAKING ANY MORE TELEVISION PROGRAMMES WITH YOU, EITHER.

RIGHT. I THINK THAT ABOUT COVERS IT.

HOW DO YOU THINK THAT WENT, THEN?

DUNNO.

HOWEVER, THE SILENCE IS RATHER PLEASANT...

THE SILENCE? OH... YOU'RE RIGHT --

SPIKE HAS STOPPED SCREAMING...

HE HADN'T BEEN BACK TO BOUREMOUTH FOR A LONG TIME. NOT SINCE HE WAS A YOUNGSTER AND WE USED TO WALK UP AND DOWN THE PROMENADE TALKING ABOUT COMEDIANS...

NO. I TELL A LIE...

HE CAME BACK WHEN HIS STEPFATHER.. WELL, COMMITTED --

HE WAS A ROCK TO HIS MOTHER THROUGH ALL THAT.

SO, Y'SEE, HE *DID* HAVE A HEART. ANYWAY, HE TURNS UP AND WANTS TO TALK ABOUT THE OLD SCULPTORS AND THE PUNCH AND JUDY MEN ON THE BEACH HERE...

"I THOUGHT HE *HATED* MR. PUNCH, SAW HIM AS SOME SORT OF PERSONAL DEMON OR WHATEVER YOU'RE HAVING YOURSELF..."

"BUT NOW HE WANTED TO MAKE A *FILM* ABOUT IT. I RECKONED THAT IF ANYONE COULD MAKE A GOOD FILM ON THAT SUBJECT, IT WOULD BE GALTON AND SIMPSON..."

I'M WORKING WITH A *DIFFERENT* WRITER NOW, GEORGE. ALL VERY WORRYING.

OH, RELAX, TONY. IF THEY'VE REPLACED GALTON AND SIMPSON THEY MUST BE *BRILLIANT*...

WHAT HAVE YOU GOT SO FAR?

YESSSS...

NOOO...

TEA'S UP!

GETTING A LOT OF WORK DONE, BOYS, I TRUST?

HERE. I'VE GOT IT.

OPENING SEQUENCE. HUSBAND AND WIFE. THE BREAKFAST TABLE.

THANKS VERY MUCH, CICELY.

NOT A WORD DO THEY SPEAK TO EACH OTHER. THEIR MARRIAGE IS DEAD.

AN ATMOSPHERE OF PROFOUND, YET UNSPOKEN, LOATHING...

WHAT DO YOU THINK?

I... MADE THIS, DID I?

THE SANDMAN HAS DEDICATED HIS LIFE TO EPHEMERAL BEAUTY, JOHN, HERE TODAY...

... GONE TOMORROW?

EXACTLY!

I WAS ALSO THINKING OF TAKING OVER FROM THE DIRECTOR, JOHN. WHAT DO YOU THINK?

OH, MY DEAR FELLOW...

228

229

WHAT'S ON THE TELLY?

AND NOW WE PRESENT *STEPTOE AND SON*, WRITTEN BY RAY GALTON AND ALAN SIMPSON...

"KNOCK KNOCK!" COMING IN!

ARE YOU DECENT?

I'VE GOT YOUR *CAHIERS DU CINEMA*, *PARIS-MATCH* AND *AIR PICTURE LIBRARY*...

THE NEWSAGENT SAYS IT MAY TAKE A WEEK TO GET *PROCEEDINGS OF THE AMERICAN PHILOSOPHICAL SOCIETY* FROM NEW YORK...

-- ANYTHING GOOD ON THE TELLY?

ACTUALLY, I HAD A LOOK AT ALAN AND RAY'S NEW SERIES...

IT'S...

IT'S BRILLIANT.

THIS IS ALL *HIS* FAULT..

IT'S A KIND OF *CURSE*, ISN'T IT? HE'S FOLLOWED ME AROUND FOR YEARS. DESTROYS *EVERYTHING*.

BUT MY DEAR FELLOW...

... YOU *WROTE* THIS FILM.

LET'S RUN AWAY.

232

TAKE SEVENTY-THREE...

ANNNNNND... *ACTION!*

HOW MANY TAKES OF THIS SCENE ARE THERE?

AND WHEN DO THE JOKES START?

COMEDY IS...

COMEDY IS...

COMEDY IS...

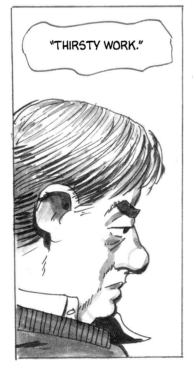

"THIRSTY WORK."

I APPEAR TO HAVE HIT HER.

CICELY OR FRED?

233

CIS.

DO YOU KNOW SHE STUDIED JUDO AS A GIRL?

BRAVO, CICELY.

DID YOU SEE THE FILM, THEN, IN THE END?

OH? HAS IT BEEN RELEASED?

YOU KNOW VERY WELL IT HAS.

OH, I MAY HAVE READ SOMETHING SOMEWHERE...

BUT NOT THE REVIEWS, I HOPE?

OH DEAR ME, NO.

NEVER MIND, EH? NEW TV SERIES ON THE HORIZON.

NOT WITH THE BBC, THOUGH. THE OTHER LOT.

I SAY! DO YOU THINK ALAN AND RAY MIGHT DO THE SCRIPTS?

HANCOCK
"THE PALLBEARER"
BY
TERRY NATION.

TONY, HAVE YOU MET WILFRID LAWSON? HE'LL BE PLAYING THE UNDERTAKER.

234

GN EEVING. HARAPOO LANCOCK FEEEEEEP

HAS HE BEEN DRINKING? I REFUSE TO COUNTENANCE SUCH UNPROFESSIONALISM.

SHALL WE HAVE THE TELLY ON, THEN? WHAT SHALL WE WATCH?

ARTHUR HAYNES IS STARTING IN A MINUTE.

ARTHUR IT IS!

ONLY ME!

DID YOU GET THE PAPER?

THEY-UH-THEY WERE SOLD OUT...

NOT TO WORRY. I POPPED OUT AND GOT ONE.

YOU... PROBABLY SHOULDN'T HAVE READ THAT...

235

TOO LATE.

"IT IS WITH UNTOLD RELIEF I CAN REPORT THAT THIS WEEK'S HANCOCK SHOW IS THE LAST AND PRODUCERS PROMISE NOT TO INFLICT ANY MORE SUCH TORTURE ON THE LONG-SUFFERING PUBLIC."

NEVER MIND, EH? YOU SAID YOU WANTED CONCENTRATE ON FILMS, ANYWAY...

THAT CONTRACT'S OFF, TOO. THEY HAVE ALL THESE LITTLE WAYS OF GETTING OUT OF THINGS.

THEY CAN'T DO THAT. SPEAK TO THEM!

WE SPOKE. IF I WANT TO PURSUE A CAREER IN THE CINEMA, THEY SUGGEST THAT I STUDY THE CROWD-PLEASING FAMILY-FRIENDLY FILMS...

... OF NORMAN FUCKING WISDOM.

MAYBE GO A LITTLE EASIER ON THAT THIS EVENING, EH?

I'LL SHOW THEM.

SERIOUSLY, TONY --

236

FRED?

FREDDIE?

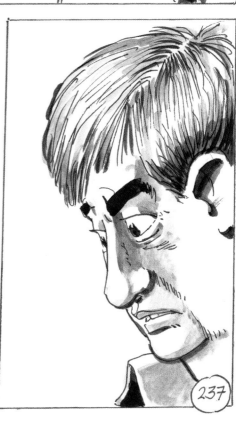

237

THIS IS WHAT I GET FOR WORRYING ABOUT YOU, IS IT?

NO. I -- FRED...

THAT'S *IT*.

THIS IS DRIVING ME MAD, TONY! AND IF YOU CAN'T SEE WHAT IT'S DOING TO YOU...

... TAKE A GOOD LOOK AND SEE WHAT IT'S DOING TO ME...

FRED...

THERE. I'M DEAD. HAPPY?

FRED. THESE PILLS...

THEY'RE LAXATIVES.

238

OH...

... SHIT.

QUITE.

OH. ALMOST FORGOT. THEY WANT ME TO GO TO AUSTRALIA TO ACCEPT SOME AWARD...

BUT I DON'T WANT TO GO.

RIGHT.

FRED?

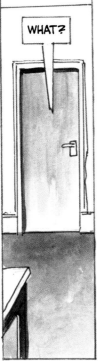

WHAT?

I'M GOING BACK TO CICELY FOR A BIT.

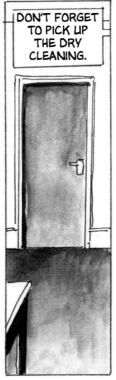

DON'T FORGET TO PICK UP THE DRY CLEANING.

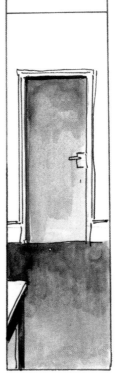

239

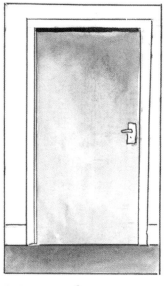 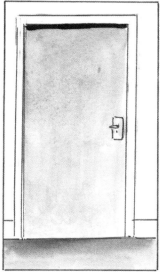  

SO...

... WE GOT MARRIED.

AS SOON AS THE DIVORCE FROM CICELY CAME THROUGH.

I MEAN... YOU COULDN'T TURN YOUR BACK ON HIM.

I COULDN'T, AT LEAST.

THE PUBLIC NEVER STOPPED LOVING HIM, EITHER.

HE DREW LOVE TO HIM LIKE A MAGNET.

HE JUST NEVER SEEMED TO KNOW WHAT TO DO WITH IT.

ALL RIGHT. THAT'S YOUR LOT.

242

YOU *WERE!* WITH THE BROKEN LEG!

YES INDEED. AND THE FUNNY THING IS...

"... IT WASN'T A GAG. I'D *REALLY* BROKEN IT!"

THE FUNNY THING IS, IT'S NOT A GAG. I'VE *REALLY* BROKEN IT!"

YOU'RE NOT ONE OF THOSE METHOD ACTOR CHAPPIES, ARE YOU?

GOOD HEAVENS, NO.

MORE OF A CASE OF *ONE OVER THE EIGHT AND ARSE OVER TIT!*

ARE YOU... WILLIE RUSHTON? THE CARTOONIST?

AND PART-TIME ACTOR, YES.

YOU DREW A SATIRICAL PIECE ABOUT ME IN *PRIVATE EYE* A FEW YEARS AGO. SUGGESTED I WAS A WASHED-UP FAKE WHOSE HAT WAS A BETTER ACTOR THAN I WAS?

YES..?

THOUGHT SO.

THAT WAS QUITE *PRESCIENT* OF YOU, WASN'T IT?

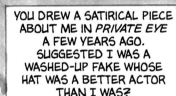

WELL, IF YOU EVER THINK OF DOING A *SEQUEL*, GIVE ME A SHOUT. I'VE SUNK A LOT FURTHER SINCE THEN. THERE'S NO END OF DIRT WITH WHICH I CAN SUPPLY YOU.

I HIT MY GIRLFRIEND. SHE'S MY WIFE NOW. AND I HIT MY WIFE, TOO. MY PREVIOUS WIFE...

HE WENT ON AND ON. AWFUL DETAILS.

WHEN A DRUNK GETS TO THE CONFESSIONAL, SELF-FLAGELLATING STAGE...

BUT I LIKED HIM.

243

I SAW HIM AND FREDDIE TOGETHER, TOO. IT WASN'T AN ACT. THEY LOVED EACH OTHER.

HERE HE IS NOW.

HE WAS ONLY -- FORTY, THEN? SOMETHING LIKE THAT.

HERE'S ANOTHER IMPRESSION FOR YOU. CHARLES LAUGHTON.

MISTAH CHRISTIAN!

NOTHING BUT TOPICAL MATERIAL TONIGHT, LADIES AND GENTLEMEN.

THE BELLS! *THE BELLS!*

GO ON THEN, ANTHONY. TELL US A JOKE.

THERE WERE THESE TWO -- NO.

THERE WAS THIS TRAVELLING SALESMAN...

THERE WAS A...

THERE WAS THIS...

BAD DREAM?

HARD TO SAY.

WELL?

SEEMS QUITE REAL. DO IT AGAIN.

EARN IT.

245

"CICELY?"

MAC CONKEY'S

MY KEY DOESN'T WORK IN THE LOCK. CICELY?

ALL RIGHT THEN...

ONCE MORE INTO THE BREACH, AND DEVIL TAKE THE HINDMOST...

WHAT IS IT, TONY?

WHAT. IS. IT. TONY. THAT'S A VERY GOOD QUESTION. ONE THAT HAS PERPLEXED THE FINEST DOCTORS IN THE FINEST DRYING-OUT CLINICS IN THIS FINE LAND. ANY CHANCE OF A DRINK?

NO.

COME ON. OLD BOOZERS LIKE US HAVE ALWAYS GOT A BOTTLE HANDY.

TONY --

WE NEED TO FINALISE A FEW THINGS.

WHAT THINGS?

DIVORCE THINGS.

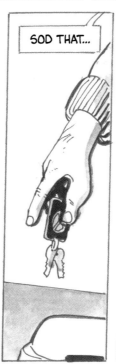

SOD THAT...

I'M OFF.

TONY!

247

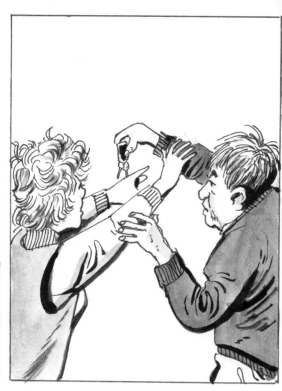

I'LL CALL YOU A TAXI.

"WHAT DID YOU DO THEN?"

I WENT TO SEE ALAN AND RAY. THOUGHT THEY MIGHT LIKE TO WRITE ME A NEW SERIES.

AND WILL THEY?

NO. LOYALTY DOESN'T SEEM TO MEAN MUCH THESE DAYS. BUT I MET SPIKE WHILE I WAS THERE.

HE WAS ON HIS WAY TO HOSPITAL, TOO. HIS *BRAIN*, Y'KNOW. SO I TOLD HIM I WAS ON MY WAY HERE -- *AGAIN* -- TO DRY OUT AND WHATNOT. AND WE LAUGHED ABOUT THAT. TWITS THAT PASS IN THE NIGHT.

WELL, WE'LL START OFF BY *BLAH-BLAH-BLAH-BLAH-BLAH. BLAH-BLAH-BLAH*

I SAY...

IS THAT? --

IS THIS? --

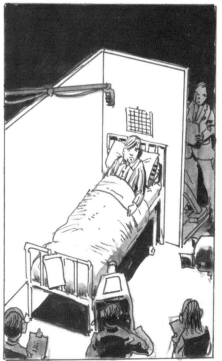

HOW-HOW LONG IS IT...

... SINCE I'VE HAD A DRINK?

ALMOST A WEEK. YOUR FRIEND SIDNEY JAMES IS WAITING DOWNSTAIRS. HE SEEMS MOST CONCERNED FOR YOU. SHALL I BRING HIM UP TO SEE YOU?

249

NO.

WE REMIND YOU THAT YOU ENTERED INTO A CONTRACT TO PERFORM THESE SHOWS AND THE DELFONT ORGANISATION WILL USE EVERY MEANS THE LAW PLACES AT ITS DISPOSAL TO SEE THAT YOU DO SO.

I THINK HE WAS AFRAID OF MONEY. LOSING IT, SPENDING IT. HE WAS ILL, BUT THE THOUGHT THAT HE MIGHT GET SUED...

WELL.

HE WENT ON THIS TOUR. THEATRES. I HADN'T SEEN HIM SINCE HIS MUM'S THIRD HUSBAND HAD DIED. I CALLED IN AT THE STAGE DOOR.

HE WOULDN'T SEE ME.

I GOT ANGRY. I SHOULDN'T HAVE.

I SHOUTED THAT I'D BEEN THERE AT THE VERY START, AND IF IT HADN'T BEEN FOR ME, COACHING AND ENCOURAGING HIM...

LIKE I SAID, I SHOULDN'T HAVE. *NOT* MY FINEST MOMENT

NOT *HIS*, EITHER, THAT TOUR.

250

LOOK AT THIS PLACE WHAT A DUMP, EH?

WHERE'S A GOOD WRECKING BALL WHEN YOU NEED ONE?

ALL RIGHT. IMPRESSIONS.

MISTAH CHRISTIAN!

CAPTAIN BLIGH, THAT WAS.

THE BELLS! THE BELLS!

DO THE BLOOD DONOR!

I THOUGHT SOME OF IT WENT REALLY WELL.

BUT WHY DO YOU NEVER STICK TO THE SCRIPT?

251

AND WHY CAN'T YOU TAKE YOUR EYES OFF THAT STAGE MANAGER?

WHAT?

IF THERE'S ONE THING I CAN'T STAND, IT'S INFIDELITY.

YOU'VE BEEN KICKING AT THE FOUNDATIONS OF THIS MARRIAGE, EVER SINCE IT STARTED. WELL, YOU'VE GOT YOUR WISH. IT'S *OVER*.

WELL, SHE'S DONE IT.

OH, MY DEAR FELLOW!

COME IN, COME IN!

GOOD OLD JOHN.

BEST PAL A BOY EVER HAD.

HE'D MET JOAN BY THIS STAGE, AND THEY'D BEGUN A RELATIONSHIP. HATTIE, JOHN'S WIFE, EVEN ENCOURAGED THEM.

HOW CIVILISED IS *THAT*, EH?

HOW DO YOU DO IT?

WHAT'S THE SECRET OF HAPPINESS?

YOU'VE CLEARLY FOUND IT. SO OUT WITH IT.

I THINK WE JUST REALISE HOW LUCKY WE ARE.

OH, *BEAUTIFULLY* PUT, JOAN-DEAR.

I'VE BEEN READING. IT'S A COLD UNIVERSE, AND IF THERE EVER WAS A GOD, HE'S DEAD, OR ELSE HE'S TODDLED OFF TO THE PUB WITH THE HOUSEKEEPING MONEY.

THAT LOVELY BRAIN OF YOURS, TONY, YOU NEED TO OCCUPY IT.

JOHN TELLS ME YOU'VE GOT ALL SORTS OF PROJECTS UP-AND-COMING...

YES INDEED. I'VE GOT HALF A DOZEN IDEAS FOR FILMS, AN IDEA FOR A TV SERIES THAT WILL CHANGE THE VERY NATURE OF THE MEDIUM. *RICHARD BURTON* WANTS TO DO SHAKESPEARE WITH ME. I'M GOING TO BECOME A CARTOONIST, OR MAYBE WORK IN COLLAGE, LIKE *MAGRITTE*. THE OLDER MAGRITTE. HE WORKED FROM HIS BED, DID YOU KNOW THAT? THAT'D SUIT ME. I THINK PERHAPS PYJAMAS MIGHT BE MY NATURAL MEDIUM.

AND YOU MUSTN'T FORGET YOUR BOOK...

YOU'RE WRITING A BOOK? WHAT'S IT ABOUT?

IT'S ABOUT *EVERYTHING*, JOAN. THE LOT.

AND HOW'S IT COMING ALONG, TONY?

WELL, I'VE GOT A *TITLE*...

"IT'S THE *RESEARCH* THAT EATS UP THE YEARS..."

44 CHARIN

HELLO!

WE MANAGED TO FIND YOU A FIRST EDITION OF *THE WIND IN THE WILLOWS*.

OH, VERY NICE!

THE LEATHER BOUND NIETZCHE MIGHT TAKE ANOTHER WEEK OR TWO, THOUGH.

KENNETH GRAHAME. HE HAD IT FIGURED OUT. UP AND DOWN THE RIVER IN YOUR LITTLE BOAT. TEA AND SANDWICHES. LITTLE CHATS THAT APPEAR TRIVIAL, BUT SOMEHOW CAST A WONDERFUL LIGHT ON THE ESSENTIAL MYSTERIES OF THE UNIVERSE. THAT'S THE WAY TO DO IT.

UM...

254

THAT'S JUST HIS *CHARACTERS*. BADGER, MOLE AND RATTY..

OH?

POOR GRAHAME HIMSELF NEVER SEEMED TO FIND WHAT HE WAS AFTER. HE HAD SO MANY IDEAS FOR OTHER BOOKS, BUT HE NEVER GOT AROUND TO WRITING ANY OF THEM. SAD, ISN'T IT?

HE WAS PARALYSED BY INFINITE POSSIBILITIES.

BUT DO YOU KNOW SOMETHING ELSE?

SUCH AS?

IF THEY EVER MAKE A FILM OF *THE WIND IN THE WILLOWS*, YOU'D MAKE A LOVELY MR. TOAD!

255

JOHN COULDN'T FRY AN EGG TO SAVE HIS LIFE.

TRUE. AND AS FOR THAT OTHER THING? WHATEVER IS IT *CALLED*?

THE WASHING MACHINE!

SIMPLY BEYOND ME.

NEVER MIND, LOVE. YOU'RE YOU, AND THAT'S WHAT COUNTS.

REALLY?

THAT'S ALL ANY OF US CAN LAY CLAIM TO, ISN'T IT?

I THINK JOAN HAS TAKEN A BIT OF SHINE TO YOU. SHE TOLD ME SHE SAW YOU BEING INTERVIEWED ON TELEVISION AND SHE JUST WANTED TO HUG YOU. ISN'T SHE A DEAR?

256

SOMETHING APPEARS TO BE EATING YOU.

WHAT DO YOU MEAN?

YOU SAY THAT YOUR HAPPINESS IS JUST AHEAD OF YOU STILL...

YES...

THERE'S SOMETHING TROUBLING YOU ABOUT THE WORLD. I'D LIKE TO KNOW WHAT IT IS.

SHE SEES YOU AS SOME SORT OF ROMANTIC FIGURE. BUT OF COURSE, THAT'S WHY I LOVE HER

I WISH I'D NEVER GIVEN THAT INTERVIEW. I THINK THAT'S WHERE IT ALL STARTED TO GO WRONG.

OH, I DON'T AGREE.

I THINK IT PROBABLY ALL STARTED TO GO WRONG WHEN YOU GOT RID OF SID. STILL, NO USE CRYING OVER SPLIT MILK, EH?

I CAN'T GET STUCK IN A RUT, REPEATING MYSELF ENDLESSLY, LIKE THOSE BLOODY COMEDY SHOWS IN AMERICA.

THAT'S *DEATH*, JOHN.

ONCE THE FORMAT BECOMES A TRAP, YOU HAVE TO SMASH IT AND MOVE ON. IF YOU WANT TO DO ANYTHING GOOD, THAT IS.

IT'S A QUESTION OF IDENTIFYING THE MAIN PROBLEM, JOHN. THE OBSTACLE TO PROGRESS AND... REMOVING IT.

I'M SURE SID UNDERSTANDS. RAY AND ALAN TOO, OF COURSE.

AND KENNY. AND HATTIE...

I WANT TO DO SOMETHING *GREAT*, JOHN.

257

MY DEAR FELLOW. YOU ALREADY *HAVE*.

'ERE. YOU'RE 'IM.

I USED TO BE.

YOU DO KNOW WHAT SORT OF PLACE THIS IS, DONCHA?

BUT DO I CARE?

TELL YOU WHAT. FIVE QUID FOR THE WORKS OR THIRTY BOB FOR A BLOW-JOB. CAN'T SAY FAIRER THAN THAT.

VERY KIND OF YOU...

BUT NOT TONIGHT CHUM, THANKS.

TRIED IT A COUPLE OF TIMES. ANY PORT IN A STORM. BUT I'M HERE TO DRINK. CAN I BUY YOU ONE?

TELL YOU WHAT, SQUIRE. LET ME BUY *YOU* A DRINK. TO SAY THANKS FOR ALL THE LAUGHS YOU'VE GIVEN ME.

MOST KIND OF YOU...

BUT I WARN YOU...

"I'M VERY THIRSTY."

TONY...

JOHN'S AWAY WORKING ON A FILM. IN FRANCE.

STILL WANT TO HUG ME?

I'M NOT SURE IF WE SLEPT TOGETHER THAT NIGHT OR THE NEXT...

I LOVED HIM.

OF COURSE YOU DID. WE BOTH DID.

I REMEMBER HIS FEET WERE HUGE. SWOLLEN, FROM THE STRAIN ON HIS HEART, PERHAPS. OR HIS LIVER?

THERE WERE FIGHTS, TOO.

DO WE REALLY NEED TO GO INTO THIS?

AND AS FOR YOUR INSISTENCE ON DEPICTING ME IN THIS COAT --

AND DO NOT, FOR ONE MOMENT, THINK I HAVE FORGOTTEN ABOUT THE HAT...

I WONDER WHO THAT CAN BE?

259

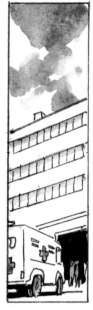

"THE LINK."

HOW'S THAT FOR A TITLE?

"THE LINK, OR: ANYONE FOR TENNIS." NEVER UNDERESTIMATE THE POWER OF A GOOD SUBTITLE...

WELL, GO ON READ US A BIT.

THE REMAINDER OF THE WORK REMAINS IN A PLASTIC STATE, AS OF THIS JUNCTURE IN TIME...

MEANING YOU HAVEN'T WRITTEN IT YET?

SO, YOU'RE THE COMEDIAN IN THE FAMILY NOW, ARE YOU?

OH, DO SHUT UP.

HE RANG ME UP TO SAY HE WANTED TO COME BACK. I BELIEVED HIM.

YOU WANTED TO SAVE HIM.

HE TELEPHONED ME AND SAID, "MUM, I'VE SEEN DAD..."

WELL, I DIDN'T NEED TO BE CONVINCED THAT THERE ARE MORE THINGS IN HEAVEN AND EARTH THAN ARE DREAMED OF BY HORATIO NELSON...

THEN HE SAYS TO ME, "I'M LEAVING HER, MUM."

"WHICH ONE?" I WANTED TO SAY, BUT I DIDN'T. BEING POLITE.

HE WAS DEPRESSED BECAUSE HE'D MADE THIS AWFUL TV SHOW. THEY HAD HIM AS A COMPERE IN A TATTY NIGHT CLUB.

BUT HE WAS SO DRUNK DURING THE SHOOTING THAT THEY'D EDITED HIM AWAY TO ALMOST *NOTHING* BY THE TIME IT WAS TRANSMITTED...

261

-- AND THE REVIEWS WERE MERCILESS.

"A PECULIAR FORM OF SUICIDE", ONE CALLED IT...

HE CALLED ME UP AND SAID HE WANTED TO COME HOME...

"WHEREVER HOME WAS."

" SO MANY CALLS, BUT HE NEVER TURNED UP...

"I THINK BY THAT STAGE, THE ONLY TIMES HE KNEW HE EXISTED WAS WHEN HE MANAGED TO UPSET PEOPLE...

"HE CALLED EVERYBODY..."

PHYLLIS?

... THEN WALT DISNEY HIRED ME.

I ALWAYS WANTED TO BE SNOW WHITE. BUT I DRIFTED.

LONG STORY SHORT. THEY SACKED ME.

HOW DARE THEY!

TO BE FAIR, I OVERDID IT WITH THE LUNCH TIME DRINKIES...

WELL, YOU'RE ONLY HUMAN, SWEETHEART!

TONY?

PHYLLIS!

262

I'VE BEEN READING. TIME REPEATS, PHYLLIS.

BUT IF YOU CAN FIND THE WRONG TURN YOU TOOK, YOU CAN UN-TAKE IT AND ESCAPE INTO THE LIFE YOU *SHOULD* HAVE HAD.

WHAT LIFE IS THAT, TONY?

EVERYTHING WAS GOOD WHEN YOU WERE MY AGENT, PHYLLIS.

I DON'T KNOW ABOUT THAT. YOU DROVE ME MAD!

BUT I FORGIVE YOU.

SO LET'S WIND THE CLOCK ALL THE WAY BACK, SHALL WE?

THE WORLD ONLY TURNS IN ONE DIRECTION AS FAR AS I KNOW...

EXACTLY!

WE ONLY NEED IT TO GO IN *ONE* DIRECTION. BACKWARDS.

AND THEN FORWARDS AGAIN, OF COURSE. PICTURE IT!

HELLO AND WELCOME TO CHRISTMAS DAY VIEWING ON BBC TELEVISION. IT'S DECEMBER 25TH 1980, AND WE'LL BE LEADING OFF TODAY WITH A SEASONAL EPISODE OF *HANCOCK'S HALF HOUR*...

DON'T YOU SEE? WE KNOW WHICH HORSE WON LAST SATURDAY'S RACE, RIGHT?

'COURSE WE DO.

WELL, ALL WE NEED TO DO IS GO BACK TO LAST FRIDAY, BACK THE WINNER, AND COLLECT ON SATURDAY!

IS THAT RIGHT?

"THE LINK" of "ANYONE FOR TENNIS"

WE JUST SEEMED TO FIGHT ALL THE TIME. I TOOK AN OVERDOSE.

OH, MY POOR DARLING...

AND ALL THE TIME, I WAS THINKING, "HOW WILL THIS AFFECT TONY?"

BUT YOU'RE BETTER NOW, DEAR HEART. YOU'RE BETTER.

YES...

AND THEN A PRODUCER IN AUSTRALIA CONTACTED PHYLLIS, HIS AGENT...

A SERIES! GOOD OLD PHYLLIS!

I TOLD YOU ABOUT CIRCULAR TIME, DIDN'T I?

NO...

WELL, I MEANT TO. ANYWAY, IT WORKS. HENCE AUSTRALIA.

I'M SORRY, I DON'T QUITE --

EVERYTHING IS REVERSED IN AUSTRALIA, ISN'T IT? IT'S DAY HERE WHEN IT'S NIGHT THERE. IF THAT'S NOT TIME GOING BACKWARDS, I DON'T KNOW WHAT IS!

I THINK HE BELIEVED IT...

AT LEAST FOR A WHILE.

265

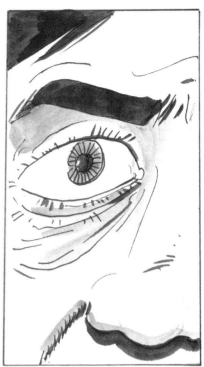

267

HERE'S TO TOMATO JUICE AND ALL WHO SAIL IN HER.

YOUR HEALTH, SIR.

DO YOU KNOW WHAT'S GREAT ABOUT AUSTRALIA, EDDIE?

APART FROM *EVERYTHING*, YOU MEAN?

HA-VERY-HA.

BUT YOU'RE THE DIRECTOR, EDDIE, AND I'M THE HUMOURIST. LET'S KEEP TO OUR RESPECTIVE FURROWS, SHALL WE?

SO WHAT'S SO GREAT ABOUT AUSTRALIA, TONY?

I'M GLAD YOU ASKED, YOUNG EDWARD.

WHAT'S GREAT ABOUT AUSTRALIA IS THAT NOBODY KNOWS ME HERE. I HAVEN'T DISAPPOINTED ANYONE YET.

ARE YOU *KIDDING?* YOUR SHOWS ARE ON TELLY HERE ALL THE TIME! THE PAPERS ARE FULL OF GOSSIP ABOUT YOU!

AH.

WHAT I MEANT TO SAY WAS, THEY *LOVE* YOU HERE.

I KNOW ALL ABOUT LOVE, EDDIE. AND WHAT HAPPENS WHEN IT'S FINISHED WITH YOU.

268

ANYTHING TO DECLARE?

JUST MY -- JUST MY...

IS ALL THIS FORGETTING HIS LINES PART OF THE JOKE? BECAUSE IT'S NOT FUNNY.

HE'S JUST WARMING UP. SETTLING IN. HE'LL BE GREAT. HE'S BEEN ILL.

ILL? *PISSED*, MORE LIKE....

I WAS NEW TO AUSTRALIA, TOO. STILL GETTING USED TO THE PLACE. *THE HEAT!*

BUT HANCOCK WORKED HARD, DESPITE HIS DEMONS. I MEAN, I COULD SEE THAT THEY WERE NEVER FAR AWAY. BUT HE CARRIED ON, AS IF IN SPITE OF THEM.

I STARTED TO REALISE THAT WE MIGHT BE MAKING SOMETHING GOOD. BUT ALL TONY HEARD WAS THAT THE MANAGEMENT WANTED TO GIVE UP ON HIM.

SO, HE STARTED TO SLIP.

DESPITE THAT, THE BOSSES DECIDED TO GO AHEAD WITH A SECOND SERIES BEFORE THE FIRST ONE WAS BROADCAST...

... IF ONLY SOMEONE HAD THOUGHT TO TELL *THAT* TO TONY...

269

NEW IN OZ?

HOW CAN YOU TELL?

YOU'RE FUNNY.

SO I'VE BEEN TOLD.

DO YOU HAVE A TELEPHONE I COULD USE, BY ANY CHANCE?

FOR YOU, SIR, ABSOLUTELY.

PHYLLIS?

TONY? HOW DID YOU FIND ME IN HONG KONG?

PHYLLIS, THIS HASN'T WORKED OUT. WE NEED TO RE-SET THE UNIVERSE AGAIN. COME QUICKLY.

YOU KNOW ALL THAT STUFF ISN'T REAL, TONY. AND BESIDES, I'M IN THE MIDDLE OF THIS ROLF HARRIS TOUR. I CAN'T JUST WALK OUT ON HIM...

ALL GOOD, MATE?

DID YOU KNOW THAT NONE OF THIS IS REAL?

TO BE HONEST, I'VE SUSPECTED SOMETHING LIKE THAT FOR A WHILE... DRINK?

WHY N -- *THERE* HE IS. SEE HIM?

SEE *WHO*, MATE?

270

"OUT! OUT ARE THE LIGHTS! OUT ALL!

"AND OVER EACH QUIVERING FORM, THE CURTAIN, A FUNERAL PALL COMES DOWN WITH THE RUSH OF A STORM!

"WHILE THE ANGELS, ALL PALLID AND *WAN*, UPRISING, UNVEILING, AFFIRM THAT THE PLAY IS THE TRAGEDY *MAN*...

"AND ITS HERO, THE CONQUEROR WORM"

YOU... LITTLE... BASTARD

LET'S SEE WHO'S BEHIND ALL THIS, SHALL WE?

LET'S GET THE MONSTER OUT IN THE OPEN!

271

"IT'S A QUESTION OF IDENTIFYING THE PROBLEM, JOHN...

"THE MAIN *OBSTACLE* TO PROGRESS...

"... AND REMOVING IT."

TONY HANCOCK TOOK HIS OWN LIFE ON 24TH JUNE 1968.

HE WAS 44 YEARS OLD.

AFTER CREMATION, THE URN CONTAINING HIS ASHES WAS ENTRUSTED TO WILLIE RUSHTON FOR THE FLIGHT HOME TO BRITAIN...

THE STORY GOES THAT THE CABIN CREW INSISTED TONY HANCOCK SHOULD FLY FIRST CLASS...

WHEN WILLIE CAME FORWARD FROM ECONOMY CLASS AT THE END OF THE JOURNEY TO COLLECT THE URN, THERE WAS A *SINGLE ROSE* ON THE SEAT BESIDE IT...

AND A NOTE.

"THANK YOU FOR MAKING US LAUGH."

STEPHEN WALSH & KEITH PAGE · DUBLIN & LONDON, 2023

274